1970

Introduction to Calculus

Introduction to Calculus

R. A. STAAL

University of Waterloo
Ontario, Canada

Dickenson Publishing Company, Inc., Belmont, California

L. C. Cat. Card No.: 66–20042
Printed in the United States of America

Preface

This book is an introduction to elementary calculus. Its primary aim is to show that the subject involves a small number of basic results having a wide variety of applications.

To achieve this aim, several things seem necessary. First, a much leaner treatment than has been current in American texts is required if the skeleton and sinews of the subject are to stand out with any degree of clarity. The book is thus not a compendium of all the most widely known results, formulas, and applications. Details not covered here can be found in any library.

Second, a closely knit presentation of the theory seems necessary if the over-all structure is to be perceptible. Such a presentation has been achieved partly by putting many of the supplementary remarks and applications into the problems section.

Third, a special approach seems needed to express clearly the relationships among differentiation, anti-differentiation, and integration, and to find a way through, or around, the well-known difficulties connected with differential notation.

The level of rigor adopted is, without apology, that of geometrical intuition (admittedly not easy to define), although some of the problems are aimed at getting the student to think about real variable matters. The main need is for a level of rigor that is recognizable and consistently maintained.

The book has been written for two groups of students, and it arose out of notes for lectures given to such groups. The first group is composed of students who probably are taking their first and last calculus course and want only a general familiarity with the subject. The second group is comprised of students with a strong mathematical interest who are headed for substantial work in analysis. For them, it serves as an intuitive survey of the ground they will subsequently cover at a much higher level of rigor, and it also provides enough practical material to take care of their immediate needs in courses

v

of an applied nature. With this second group, the text is covered much more rapidly, and a much greater proportion of time is spent on the more challenging problems. For neither group should the omission of exercises on, for example, the formula for $D_x \operatorname{cosech}^{-1} u$ be of any consequence!

I would like to express my indebtedness to the many students whose responsiveness has done much to determine the final form of this book. I am especially indebted to Dr. R. L. Jeffery and Dr. R. L. Rosenberg, who have made many invaluable comments concerning the text and the problems of teaching elementary calculus.

R. A. Staal

Contents

Introduction to Calculus

1

The Limit Concept

In the days before calculus, one did not have to go very far in certain directions in mathematics to reach an impasse. Progress resulted only when the stumbling blocks were seen not as an impasse but as the source of a new mathematical idea; and when that new idea was understood and developed, a new branch of mathematics was created.

A few examples will illustrate the kinds of difficulties that led to the development of calculus.

1.1 The Area of a Curved Region

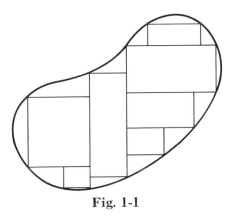

Fig. 1-1

If we wish to find the area of a curved region (Fig. 1-1), it is natural to try to divide the region into rectangles and add up their areas. The difficulty is that a curved region cannot be divided exactly into rectangles: no matter how small we make the rectangles, there are always curved regions left over. And no matter how far we carry the subdivision, the combined areas of all the rectangles will always be less than the area of the given region. It seems that the area cannot be determined in this way.

However, in attempting to determine area in this way an important observation can be made—one that will eventually lead to the solution of the problem: *the more rectangles we use, the closer we get to the required area.* Furthermore, *by using enough rectangles we can get as close to the actual area as we like.* (We are assuming an intuitive understanding of what is meant by area. Later, we will use this idea of splitting into rectangles to *define* the concept of area.)

The italicized remark above is our introduction to the notion on which calculus is founded—that of a *limit*. We can summarize the situation above by saying that *as we take more and more rectangles, the sum of their areas approaches the required area as limit* (more precisely, the area is *defined* to be this limit). The problem is to find this limit.

1.2 Speed

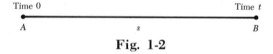

Fig. 1-2

The everyday concept of speed leads to difficulties similar to those encountered in Fig. 1-2, although we do not ordinarily think carefully enough about the matter to notice this. What do we mean by speed? How do we measure it?

Consider a point moving along a straight line. Suppose we want to know its speed at the instant it is at A. The usual procedure is to measure the distance s it travels in time t: we then say that its *average* speed during the time interval t is

$$\frac{\text{distance travelled}}{\text{time taken}} = \frac{s}{t}$$

This may not be the actual speed at A, however, as the speed may have changed during the journey from A to B. Our intuition tells us that if we take smaller and smaller intervals of time, then s/t will get closer and closer to the actual speed at A. By making t sufficiently small, we can make the possible change in speed between A and B, and hence the error of our estimation, as small as we like.

We summarize all this by saying that *as t approaches* 0, *s/t approaches the speed at A as limit.* (We assume here an intuitive understanding of what we mean by speed. What we could do is to use the limit concerned to *define* the notion of speed.)

It is to be emphasized that, in general, *no* value of *t*, no matter how small, makes *s/t* the actual speed. If we make *t* zero, then *s* is zero, which is a useless situation. Thus the problem of finding the limit is far from trivial.

1.3 Work

The physical concept of work involves the same difficulties we met in 1.1 unless we confine ourselves to the very simplest cases.

If a constant force F acts through a distance, s (in the direction of the force), then the work done is $F \cdot s$. If, as often happens, the force varies while it acts, the situation is not so simple.

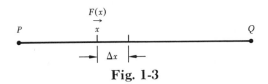

Fig. 1-3

Suppose a particle is moved by a varying force $F(x)$ from P to Q (Fig. 1-3). We write "$F(x)$" to indicate that the magnitude of the force depends on the point x at which it is acting. If we simply multiply the force at P by the distance PQ, we will not (except by coincidence) arrive at the actual work done, since the force F changes during the journey from P to Q.

We can, however, take into account the varying of the force in the following way: we break the interval PQ into many little intervals, estimate the work done over each of these small intervals, and add up the results.

In more detail, let Δx be the length of a typical little interval, let x be the point at its left end, and $F(x)$ the value of F at x. We use $F(x) \cdot \Delta x$ as an estimate of the work done while the particle traverses this little interval. This will not be exactly the work done, since F varies even during this little journey. However, if Δx is very small, then the force will not change much, and $F(x) \cdot \Delta x$ will not be much in error. Furthermore, by using the actual values of F at the endpoints of all the little intervals from P to Q, we take into account fairly well the changes in F.

Putting all these considerations together, we are led to the following observation (on intuitive grounds): let $\Sigma F(x) \cdot \Delta x$ be the sum of all the estimates corresponding to the small portions of the interval PQ; then, the more intervals we divide PQ into, the closer does $\Sigma F(x) \cdot \Delta x$ get to the actual work done. Furthermore, by using enough intervals, and making them small enough, we can get arbitrarily close to the work done by F. We summarize this by saying that *as we take a finer and finer decomposition of PQ, $\Sigma F(x) \cdot \Delta x$ approaches the work done as limit.*

1.4 The Tangent to a Curve

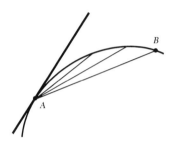

Fig. 1-4

Similar difficulties occur in the geometrical notion of the tangent to a curve (Fig. 1-4). We may imagine ourselves placing a straight line on a curve in such a way that it "just touches" the curve, and we then say that the line is "tangent to" the curve. But if we try to explain what we mean by "just touches," we see that more explanation is required.

Suppose we want to determine a tangent to a given curve at a point A. What we can do is to take a point B on the curve, near A, and join AB. This gives a secant to the curve. To get a good approximation to the tangent at A, we take B very close to A. The clue to what is meant by the tangent at A is that, *as B approaches A, the secant, AB, approaches the tangent as limit.*

We cannot simply take B to be A, for then we have only one point, which is not enough to determine a line.

1.5 The Problems of Limits in General

The preceding examples are just a few chosen at random from a great many of the same kind. In each case our goal is a certain entity, or quantity—an area, a speed, and so on. In each case we are led to a *procedure which brings us arbitrarily close to what we are after*, yet which never actually gives it to us directly. We set up *a limiting process*—can we find the limit?

This is the problem which led to the invention, or discovery, of calculus. It was noticed that two kinds of limiting processes occurred with notable frequency, and were of very special importance. (One occurs in Sections 1.1 and 1.3, and the other in Sections 1.2 and 1.4). Finally, a very powerful technique was developed for evaluating limits of these kinds.

So far we have discussed limiting processes in a general, qualitative manner. In the following examples, by the use of a little algebra, or geometry, we shall determine the limit concerned. This will lend some hope to our being able to evaluate limits such as we have just encountered.

1.6 The Geometric Series

The terms a, ar, ar^2, ar^3, $\ldots$, ar^n, $\ldots$ form an infinite sequence. The sum of the first n of these terms is

$$S_n = a\,\frac{(1-r^n)}{1-r} = \frac{a}{1-r} - \frac{ar^n}{1-r}.$$

Consider what happens to S_n as n gets larger and larger, in the case where $0 < r < 1$. As n increases, $ar^n/(1-r)$ decreases: it is never zero, but, by taking n sufficiently large, we can make it as close to zero as we like. Hence, as n increases indefinitely, S_n *approaches* $a/(1-r)$ *as limit*.

As an example, consider the case where $a = 1$ and $r = \frac{1}{2}$. We then have

$$S_n = 1 + \frac{1}{2} + \frac{1}{4} + \frac{1}{8} + \cdots + \frac{1^{n-1}}{2}.$$

Successive values of S_n can be represented as follows:

$$S_1 = 1$$

$$S_2 = 1 + \frac{1}{2}$$

$$S_3 = 1 + \frac{1}{2} + \frac{1}{4}$$

$$S_4 = 1 + \frac{1}{2} + \frac{1}{4} + \frac{1}{8}$$

$$S_5 = 1 + \frac{1}{2} + \frac{1}{4} + \frac{1}{8} + \frac{1}{16}$$

etc.

S_n approaches 2 as limit. This is fairly obvious from the picture, $ar^n/(1-r)$ taking in succession the values 1, 1/2, 1/4, 1/8, $\ldots$.

1.7 General Theorems Regarding Limits

While the emphasis in this book is on an intuitive treatment of the subject, and we do not attempt a rigorous analysis of the idea of a limit, still a few words seem in order to try to make clear what kinds of results we will assume are intuitively understandable, and to prevent our intuition from being *too* naive.

This book has to do (unless otherwise specified) with *real-valued functions of a real variable* (or variables). What are these? If there is a rule, prescription, or formula which assigns to every real number x (or possibly every member of a selected set of real numbers) a real number, then we say that this assignment determines (or is) a *real-valued function of the real variable x*. We usually denote the function by a letter, such as "f," "F," "g," etc., and the value it assigns to x by "$f(x)$," "$F(x)$," "$g(x)$," etc.

Such assignments, or functions, are frequently given via formulas or expressions such as $x^2 + 3x$, $x \cdot \sin 2x$. It is usually then the practice to refer to, for example, "the function $x^2 + 3x$," meaning "the function which assigns $x^2 + 3x$ to every x." This is simply a matter of abbreviation by the customary device of leaving certain phrases understood. In such a case there may be no need (depending on the application) for notations of the type "$f(x)$."

We will frequently refer to the *limit approached by $f(x)$ as x approaches the value a*, conveniently abbreviated by $\lim_{x \to a} f(x)$.

While this verbal statement is perhaps sufficiently suggestive on most occasions, a sharper version should be available on reserve.

"$\lim_{x \to a} f(x) = L$" means that, given any positive number ϵ, no matter how small, there exists a positive number δ (its value depending on the value of ϵ) such that, whenever x is within δ of a, then $f(x)$ is within ϵ of L (Fig. 1-5).

Fig. 1-5

Note: The value of $f(x)$ at $x = a$ is excluded from consideration.

In less precise language, "$\lim_{x \to a} f(x) = L$" means that we can keep $f(x)$ as close as we like to L by keeping x sufficiently close to (but not equal to) a.

As an example, consider the function $f(x)$ defined by

$$f(x) = x^2 \text{ for } x \neq 0,$$
$$f(0) = 1.$$

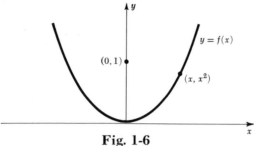

Fig. 1-6

In Fig. 1-6, provided we ignore the point $(0,1)$, we can keep $f(x)$ within ϵ of 0 by keeping $x(\neq 0)$ within a suitably chosen δ of 0. Hence $\lim_{x \to 0} f(x)$ exists and is 0.

$f(x)$ is said to be *continuous at* $x = a$ if $\lim_{x \to a} f(x)$ *exists and is equal to* $f(a)$. The above $f(x)$ is thus *discontinuous at* $x = 0$, for the limit is 0, while $f(0) = 1$.

It helps in clarifying the idea to consider a case in which $f(x)$ *does not have* a limit as x approaches a (Fig. 1-7).

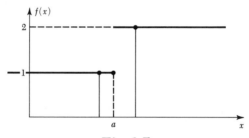

Fig. 1-7

Take $f(x) = 1$ for $x \leqslant a$, and $f(x) = 2$ for $x > a$. Then $f(x)$ *approaches no limit* as x approaches a, for in any interval surrounding a there will be x's for which $f(x) = 2$ and x's for which $f(x) = 1$, so there can be no L to which $f(x)$ can be as close as we like for *all* x's sufficiently near a.

Generally, a function fails to approach a limit as x approaches a given value whenever there is a jump or a break in its graph at the place corresponding to that value. It also fails to approach a limit if it increases beyond all bounds.

Yet another way in which this may happen is illustrated by $f(x)$ defined by

$$f(x) = \sin 1/x \text{ for } x \neq 0,$$
$$f(0) = 0,$$
$$y = f(x).$$

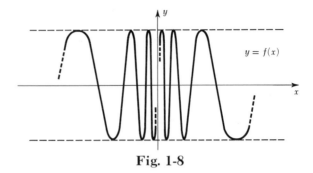

Fig. 1-8

Figure 1-8 shows that $f(x)$ attains both values 1, −1 infinitely often between any value (for x) $a \neq 0$ and 0, and hence obviously cannot be kept within ϵ of any value by keeping x sufficiently close to 0, as long as $\epsilon < 1$.

It is also customary to speak of the *limit of a convergent sequence of numbers.*

$$a_1, a_2, a_3, \cdots, a_n, \cdots$$

is said to be a *convergent sequence* if, for *every* $\epsilon > 0$, no matter how small, an interval of length ϵ can be laid down somewhere on the real axis such that all a's from a certain point on (that is, all but a finite number of them) lie within this interval (Fig. 1-9).

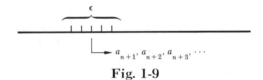

Fig. 1-9

A fundamental assumption which we make about our real number system is that *every convergent sequence has a limit which is itself a real number.* For L to be the limit of the sequence $a_1, a_2, a_3, \cdots, a_n, \cdots$ means that the above interval of length ϵ can always be taken to include L. By taking a sequence of smaller and smaller ϵ's, we get a set of intervals which "shrink" to the point L (Fig. 1-10).

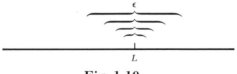

Fig. 1-10

Further discussion of these topics will occur as the need arises.

We will assume that the reader regards statements such as the following as being intuitively evident: if a and b approach A and B as limits, then $a+b$, $a-b$, $a \cdot b$, a/b approach $A+B$, $A-B$, $A \cdot B$, A/B as limits, respectively. (In the last case we assume $b \neq 0$ and $B \neq 0$). We have already used such results, and will from time to time use others which are equally evident on intuitive grounds. (In more rigorous treatments where the notion of limit is analysed much more carefully, these results are theorems that can be proved.)

1.8 The Limit of a/b as a, b Tend to Zero: Trivial Limits

One of the most important types of limits is the limit of a/b where a and b both approach zero. Most of the troublesome limits with which we deal are either of this type, or can be reduced to it.

The beginner usually expects that, since a and b approach the same limit, a/b must therefore approach 1 as limit. This is not so, for the limit of a/b depends entirely on how a and b approach zero. For example

(i) Consider a^2/a as a approaches 0. $a^2/a=a$, so a^2/a approaches 0 as limit (Fig. 1-11).

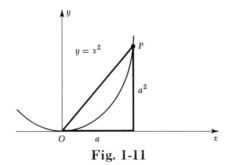

Fig. 1-11

Graphing a^2 as ordinate and a as abscissa, we see that $a^2/a=$ slope of chord OP, which approaches 0 as $a \to 0$ since the tangent at O is horizontal.

(ii) Consider a/a^2, as a approaches O. $a/a^2=1/a$, which increases beyond all bounds as a approaches O and hence approaches no limit at all (Fig. 1-12).

Graphing a as ordinate and a^2 as abscissa, we see that $a=$ slope of chord OP, which increases beyond all bounds as $a \to 0$ since the tangent approaches perpendicularity to the horizontal axis as P approaches O.

(iii) Consider $\sin x/x$ as x approaches zero (Fig. 1-13). Our experiences in (i) and (ii) should prevent us from jumping to any conclusions. The evaluation of this limit requires some care.

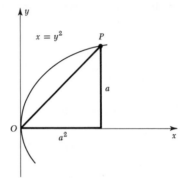

Fig. 1-12

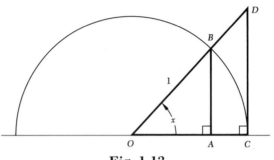

Fig. 1-13

In a circle of unit radius, let COB be an angle of x radians. Then $AB = \sin x$, $OA = \cos x$ and $CD = \tan x$. From the drawing, it is clear that area of triangle $AOB <$ area of sector $COB <$ area of triangle COD; that is, $(1/2) \cos x \sin x < x/2 < (1/2) \tan x$.

Hence, $\cos x < x/\sin x < 1/\cos x$.

Now, $\cos x$ approaches 1 as x approaches O.

Hence, $x/\sin x$ (and similarly its reciprocal) approaches 1 also, but not simply because x and $\sin x$ both approach the same limit.

So far, for the sake of emphasis, we have confined ourselves to limiting processes which never actually "reach" their limit; most of the limits which interest us are of this kind. The notion of limit however, includes such trivial cases as

$$\lim_{x \to 1} x^3 = 1, \lim_{x \to 3} \frac{2x+1}{x} = \frac{7}{3}$$

(the notation is self-explanatory)—that is to say, cases where one can actually "reach" the limit (for example, by setting $x = 1$ in x^3).

It has been seen how the notation of limit arises out of certain problems, and how limits can be evaluated in a few special cases.

The main problem is to see if the limits arising out of situations such as in Sections 1.1 through 1.4 can be evaluated, and to try to develop an efficient technique for solving such problems. It is to be noted that these limits are essentially of two kinds. One is the *limit of a ratio*, where numerator and denominator both approach zero, and the other is the *limit of a sum*, where the quantities added approach zero, but where we take more and more of them. These are both limiting processes of a non-trivial kind.

When our technique has been developed, we will have in our hands the key to the solution of a very large class of problems involving length, area, volume, acceleration, rate of change, curvature, force, pressure, work, moments—and many other physical and mathematical concepts. More important still, our understanding of these things will be much deeper.

The heart of all these problems, and the key to their solution, is the mathematical concept of limit.

Exercises*

1. Using tables, compute $\sin x/x$ for $x=1$, $\pi/6$, $\pi/60$, $\pi/600$.

2. Evaluate: (a) $\lim\limits_{x\to 0} x^2+5x+1$,

   (b) $\lim\limits_{x\to 3} \dfrac{1}{x^3-4}$,

   (c) $\lim\limits_{x\to 0} k\dfrac{\sin x}{x}$,

   (d) $\lim\limits_{x\to 0} \dfrac{\sin 5x}{x}$.

3. Using tables, compute $(1+1/n)^n$ for $n=2$, 10, 100.
   Compute also by using the first few terms of the binomial expansion.

4. Using tables, compute $(1-\cos x)/x$ for $x=1$, $\pi/6$, $\pi/60$, $\pi/600$.

5. Draw on graph paper a circle of radius 3 inches. By counting squares of sides ½ inch which lie entirely within the circle, estimate the area of the circle, and hence estimate π. Do the same with sides ¼ inch.

Problems

6. (a) Find $\lim\limits_{x\to 0} \dfrac{1-\cos x}{x}$ $\left(\text{use the result of } \dfrac{\sin x}{x}\right)$.

   (b) Find $\lim\limits_{x\to 0} \dfrac{\tan x}{x}$.

   (c) Find $\lim\limits_{x\to 0} \dfrac{1-\cos x}{\sin x}$.

* A distinction is made between exercises and problems, which it is hoped the reader will find useful. Exercises provide routine practice, and the reader isn't expected to find difficulty with them; on the other hand, the degree of difficulty of the problems varies considerably, and the reader shouldn't be discouraged if he fails to solve some of them. The problems are not arranged according to difficulty, and the reader must always be on the alert for an easy solution.

7. A point moves along the x-axis in such a way that $x = t^2$, where x is in feet and t in seconds. Find:
   (a) the distance travelled between times $t = 1$ and 1.2.
   (b) the distance travelled between times $t = 1$ and $1 + k$.
   In each case find the corresponding average speed. By letting k approach 0 in (b), find the exact speed at time $t = 1$.

8. A point $B(x, y)$ moves along the curve $y = x^2$ toward the point $A(1, 1)$. Express the slope of the chord AB in terms of x. Find the limit of this slope as B approaches A. Check approximately by drawing a graph of $y = x^2$, drawing the tangent at A, and measuring its slope.

9. The lines $y = 3x$, $x = 1$ and the x-axis form a triangle. The base (from $x = 0$ to 1) is divided into n equal parts. On the last $n - 1$ of these as bases, rectangles are drawn, each touching the hypotenuse at its upper left corner.
   (a) Find the sum of the areas of the rectangles for $n = 5, 10, K$.
   (b) What does the last sum approach as K increases indefinitely? Check by a triangular area formula.

10. Evaluate ("$x \to \infty$" signifies that x increases beyond all bounds). Hint: divide top and bottom by suitable powers of x.
    (a) $\lim\limits_{x \to 0} \dfrac{x^3 + 3x}{4x^2 + x}$,
    (b) $\lim\limits_{x \to 0} \dfrac{3x^3 + 2x^2}{x^5 - 7x^2 + x}$,
    (c) $\lim\limits_{x \to \infty} \dfrac{3x^3 + 2x^2}{x^5 - 7x^2 + x}$,
    (d) $\lim\limits_{x \to \infty} \dfrac{1 + 2x + x^3}{x - x^2}$.

11. If $f(x) = x^3 + 2x + 3$, find:
    (a) $\lim\limits_{x \to 2} f(2x)$,
    (b) $f(\lim\limits_{x \to 2} 2x)$.

12. $f(x)$ is defined as being 0 when $x \neq 0$ and 1 when $x = 0$. Find:
    (a) $\lim\limits_{x \to 0} f(x)$,
    (b) $f(\lim\limits_{x \to 0} x)$.

13. Let $g(x)$ be the smallest integer greater than x. Let $x \to a+$ mean that x approaches a *from above* (i.e., ranging through values greater than a) and let $x \to a-$ mean that x approaches a *from below*. Find:
    (a) $\lim\limits_{x \to 1/2+} g(x)$,
    (b) $\lim\limits_{x \to 1/2-} g(x)$,
    (c) $\lim\limits_{x \to 0+} g(x)$,
    (d) $\lim\limits_{x \to 0-} g(x)$,
    (e) $g(\lim\limits_{x \to 0+} x)$,
    (f) $g(\lim\limits_{x \to 0-} x)$.
    Repeat (a) to (f) using $h(x)$ instead of $g(x)$, where $h(x)$ is the greatest integer less than x.

14. Find $\lim\limits_{x \to 0} \dfrac{\sin 5x}{\sin 3x}$.

2

The Derivative

In this chapter we shall make a detailed study of one of the limiting processes introduced in Chapter 1, and, in so doing, set up one of the main pillars of the structure known as calculus.

To avoid complications, *it will be assumed from here on* that all functions mentioned (unless otherwise stated) are such that their graphs are *smooth* and *continuous*. This means that they do *not* have graphs such as that shown in Fig. 2-1. In that figure, the graph is

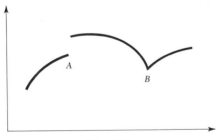

Fig. 2-1

discontinuous at *A*. At *B* it is continuous but not smooth. Continuity was discussed in Chapter 1. Later we shall be able to replace the vague notion of smoothness by that of the existence of a derivative, or of a continuous derivative.

2.1 Speed: The Slope of a Curve

In Section 1.2 we saw that the concept of speed was connected with a certain limiting process. Let us formulate the problem precisely:

position O $g(t)$ $g(t+h)$

Suppose a point moves along a straight line in such a way that its distance from a fixed point O is a given function of time t, say $g(t)$, and suppose we want to know its speed at time t. If a time interval h elapses, the point travels a distance $g(t+h) - g(t)$, and the average speed during this interval is (by definition)

$$\frac{g(t+h) - g(t)}{h}.$$

Our intuition tells us that this ratio approaches a definite limit as h tends to zero, and this limit is what we mean by the speed at time t. Thus

$$\text{speed} = \lim_{h \to 0} \frac{g(t+h) - g(t)}{h}.$$

Next, let us turn to the notion of the tangent to a curve, as in Section 1.4. Let us try to find the *slope* of the tangent to a given curve at a given point on it.

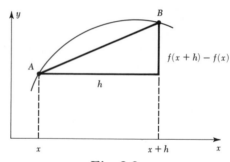

Fig. 2-2

Consider a curve whose equation is $y = f(x)$, and a point A on it, with x-coordinate x. Let B be a neighboring point on the curve, with x-coordinate $x + h$. The slope of the chord AB is

$$\frac{f(x+h) - f(x)}{h}.$$

As B approaches A, h approaches zero, and the slope of AB approaches

$$\lim_{h \to 0} \frac{f(x+h) - f(x)}{h}.$$

This limit is what we mean by the slope of the tangent at A. Comparison with the limit which gave the speed of a moving point shows that the two are identical—apart from using f instead of g and x instead of t. Evaluating limits of this kind is known as *differentiation*, and the result is called the *derivative* of the function concerned.

2.2 The Derivative

Let $f(x)$ be a function of x; that is, suppose that there is some rule, or formula, which assigns to each value of x (possibly restricted to some range of values) a number, and that we denote the number assigned to x by "$f(x)$." For example, $f(x)$ may be $\sin x + x^2$ or it may be the height in inches of a certain person at age x years.

If to each value of x over a certain range there corresponds a value of

$$\lim_{h \to 0} \frac{f(x+h) - f(x)}{h},$$

also written

$$\lim_{\Delta x \to 0} \frac{\Delta f}{\Delta x}$$

($\Delta f, \Delta x$, being the increases in f and x), then we say that $f(x)$ is *differentiable* over that range.

This limit thus determines a function of x, which we call *the derivative of $f(x)$ with respect to x* and which we denote by

$$D_x f(x) \quad \text{or} \quad f'(x).$$

Frequently the variable quantity $f(x)$ is denoted by a single letter, say "y," and the derivative is then written as

$$D_x y \quad \text{or} \quad y'.$$

When an expression of this kind occurs, it is understood that the variable, y, is some differentiable function of x. We will confine our attention in this book, unless otherwise stated, to functions which are differentiable wherever they are defined, except possibly at a finite number of points to which attention will be called.

The derivative of $f(x)$ with respect to x may be thought of as the *instantaneous* (as distinguished from average) *rate of increase of $f(x)$ with respect to x*, for it is got by dividing an increase in $f(x)$ by the corresponding increase in x, and then taking the limit of this ratio as the increases approach zero. If $f(x)$ happens to be *decreasing* as x increases, then this limit turns out to be *negative* (or possibly zero).

The problem at once arises of being able to compute the derivatives of the familiar functions of x. For example, what are $D_x x^3$, $D_x \sin x$, $D_x \sqrt{x}$? We begin with a few simple cases, and then deal with the problem in a general way.

2.3 The Derivatives of x^2, $K \cdot f(x)$, K, and x (with Respect to x)

(i)
$$D_x x^2 = \lim_{h \to 0} \frac{(x+h)^2 - x^2}{h}$$
$$= \lim_{h \to 0} \frac{x^2 + 2xh + h^2 - x^2}{h}$$
$$= \lim_{h \to 0} 2x + h$$
$$= 2x .$$

(ii) Consider a constant, K. Then, when x increases from x to $x+h$, $K \cdot f(x)$ increases from $K \cdot f(x)$ to $K \cdot f(x+h)$, hence

$$D_x \, K \cdot f(x) = \lim_{h \to 0} \frac{K \cdot f(x+h) - K \cdot f(x)}{h}$$
$$= \lim_{h \to 0} \frac{K[f(x+h) - f(x)]}{h}$$
$$= K \lim_{h \to 0} \frac{f(x+h) - f(x)}{h}$$
$$= K \cdot D_x f(x).$$

(iii) If K is a constant, then $D_x \, K = 0$. (Proof is left to the reader). This can be seen geometrically from the graph of $y = K$ (Fig. 2-3).

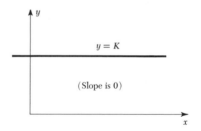

Fig. 2-3

(iv)
$$D_x x = \lim_{h \to 0} \frac{x + h - x}{h}$$
$$= \lim_{h \to 0} 1$$
$$= 1.$$

(The geometrical interpretation is left to the reader.)

Exercises

1. As in Section 2.3, use the definition of the derivative to find, from first principles,

(a) $D_x x^3$,   (b) $D_x(x^2+x^3)$,   (c) $D_x(5x^2+2x^3)$.

Check your result in (a) by drawing tangents to a graph of x^3 at points where $x = -1, 0, 2$.

2.4 Rules for Differentiating Sums, Differences, Products, and Quotients

The simplest functions are those built up out of a variable, say x, and constants, by means of the operations $+, -, \times, \div$. If differentiation rules can be developed for each of these operations, then one should be able to differentiate any function built up by means of them. Such functions are called "rational" functions, and can always be put into the form $P(x)/Q(x)$ where $P(x), Q(x)$ are polynomials.

(i) Consider $f(x) + g(x)$. If the value of x changes from x to $x + \Delta x$, then $f(x), g(x)$ change from f, g to what we call $f + \Delta f, g + \Delta g$ (thus $\Delta f, \Delta g$ are the corresponding increments in f and g; we are omitting the x's for brevity). Hence

$$D_x\,[f(x) + g(x)] = \lim_{\Delta x \to 0} \frac{(f+\Delta f) + (g+\Delta g) - (f+g)}{\Delta x}$$
$$= \lim_{\Delta x \to 0} \left[\frac{\Delta f}{\Delta x} + \frac{\Delta g}{\Delta x}\right]$$
$$= D_x f + D_x g.$$

Similarly, by replacing $+$ by $-$, we prove that

$$D_x\,[f(x) - g(x)] = D_x f(x) - D_x g(x).$$

Similar results hold for any succession of sums and differences.

(ii) Consider $f(x) \cdot g(x)$. As the value of x changes to $x + \Delta x$, this becomes $(f + \Delta f)\,(g + \Delta g)$. Hence

$$D_x f(x) \cdot g(x) = \lim_{\Delta x \to 0} \frac{(f+\Delta f)\,(g+\Delta g) - f\cdot g}{\Delta x}$$
$$= \lim_{\Delta x \to 0} \frac{f\Delta g + g\Delta f + \Delta f\Delta g}{\Delta g}$$
$$= \lim_{\Delta x \to 0} \left[f\frac{\Delta g}{\Delta x} + g\frac{\Delta f}{\Delta x} + \Delta f\cdot\frac{\Delta g}{\Delta x}\right]$$
$$= f D_x g + g D_x f.$$

(iii) The reader should now be able to prove that

$$D_x \frac{f(x)}{g(x)} = \frac{g D_x f - f D_x g}{g^2}.$$

Since it is known that D_x constant $= 0$ and $D_x x = 1$, it is now possible to differentiate any rational function of x.

For example,

$$D_x x^2 = D_x x \cdot x$$
$$= x D_x x + x D_x x \qquad \text{(product rule)}$$
$$= x + x$$
$$= 2x \qquad \text{(proven in another manner in Section 2.3),}$$
$$D_x \ 4x^2 + 3x = D_x \ 4x^2 + D_x \ 3x \qquad \text{(sum rule)}$$
$$= 4 D_x x^2 + x^2 D_x 4 + 3 D_x x + x D_x 3 \qquad \text{(product rule)}$$
$$= 4 \cdot 2x + 0 + 3 \cdot 1 + 0$$
$$= 8x + 3$$

$$D_x \frac{x+1}{x^2+x} = \frac{(x^2+x) \ D_x \ (x+1) - (x+1) \ D_x \ (x^2+x)}{(x^2+x)^2} \qquad \text{(quotient rule)}$$
$$= \frac{(x^2+x)(D_x x + D_x 1) - (x+1)(D_x x^2 + D_x x)}{(x^2+x)^2} \qquad \text{(sum rule)}$$
$$= \frac{(x^2+x) \cdot 1 - (x+1)(2x+1)}{(x^2+x)^2}$$
$$= \frac{-1}{x^2} \ .$$

(*Exercise:* Obtain also by simplifying before differentiating.)

Exercises

1. Given $f(x) = 2x^2$, $g(x) = 3/x + x$, find
   (a) $f'(1)$,   (b) $f'(3)$,
   (c) $g'(2)$,   (d) $g'(1/k)$.

2. Find, using appropriate formulas, the derivatives with respect to x of:
   (a) $1/x$,   (b) $-1/x^2$,
   (c) x^3 (treat it as xx^2),   (d) $\dfrac{2x-3}{x-6x^2}$,
   (e) $3x^2 + \dfrac{4}{x-x^2}$.

Problems

3. Find $\lim\limits_{h \to 0} \dfrac{|x+h| - |x|}{h}$, (a) when x is positive, (b) when x is negative.
   (c) Discuss the case where $x = 0$.

4. Prove the formula for differentiating a quotient of two functions.

5. (a) Prove that $D_x \ [f(x) \ g(x) \ h(x)] = (D_x f) \ gh + f(D_x g)h + fg(D_x h)$.
   (b) State and prove the general result involving a product of n functions.

6. Prove that $x^2 \sin 1/x$ has a derivative at the origin but that its derivative

is not continuous at the origin. *Hint:* for $x \neq 0$ calculate the derivative in the usual way and consider its values for $1/x$ equal to even and odd multiples of π. For $x = 0$ calculate $\lim\limits_{h \to 0} \dfrac{h^2 \sin 1/h - 0}{h}$.

2.5 The Differentiation of x^n (for n an Integer)

(i) *If n is a positive integer,* then

$$D_x x^n = \lim_{h \to 0} \frac{(x+h)^n - x^n}{h}$$

$$= \lim_{h \to 0} \frac{x^n + n\,x^{n-1}h + [n(n-1)]/1 \cdot 2\; x^{n-2}h^2 + \cdots + h^n - x^n}{h}$$

(by the binomial theorem)

$$= \lim_{h \to 0} \left[nx^{n-1} + \frac{n(n-1)}{1 \cdot 2}\,x^{n-2}h + \cdots + h^{n-1} \right]$$

$$= nx^{n-1}.$$

(ii) *If n is a negative integer,* then *the same formula holds.* Let $n = -m$, where m is a positive integer. Then

$$D_x x^n = D_x \frac{1}{x^m}$$

$$= \frac{x^m D_x 1 - 1 \cdot D_x x^m}{x^{2m}}$$

$$= \frac{0 - mx^{m-1}}{x^{2m}} \qquad \text{[by (i)]}$$

$$= -mx^{-m-1}$$

$$= nx^{n-1}.$$

To prove that the formula holds for all values of n, other methods are needed. (See Section 2.15).

Problems

1. (a) Prove Leibniz's formula

$$D_x^n(uv) = D_x^n u \cdot v + C(n,1)\,D_x^{n-1}u \cdot D_x v + C(n,2)\,D_x^{n-2}u \cdot D_x^2 v + \cdots$$
$$+ C(n,r)\,D_x^{n-r}u \cdot D_x^r v + \cdots + u \cdot D_x^n v,$$

where the C's are the binomial coefficients.
(b) Use the Pascal triangle to write down the expansion of $D_x^6(uv)$.

2. Assuming the rule for differentiating products, prove *by induction* that $D_x x^n = nx^{n-1}$ for all positive integers n.

2.6 A Note Concerning Variables

It is important to note that the name of the variable is immaterial in a differentiation formula. Thus

$$D_x x^3 + 6x = 3x^2 + 6,$$
$$D_s s^3 + 6s = 3s^2 + 6,$$
$$\frac{D}{\sqrt{\sin z}}\ (\sqrt{\sin z})^3 + 6\sqrt{\sin z} = 3\sqrt{\sin z^2} + 6.$$

(We must, of course, interchange variables *consistently* throughout; if x is replaced by s, this must be done *wherever* x appears.)

Exercises

1. Find:
   (a) $D_x\,(3x + x^2)$,   (b) $D_t\,(3t + t^2)$,
   (c) $D_x{}^2\,(3x^2 + x^4)$,   (d) $D_\theta\,1/1 - \theta$.

2. Find the derivatives with respect to x of:
   (a) x^5,   (b) x^{-5},
   (c) $1/x$ (treat it as x^{-1}), (d) $2x^7 + 4/x^9$.

2.7 Higher Order Derivatives

Before going on to differentiate more of the familiar functions, let us think a little more about derivatives in general.

The result of differentiating a function of x with respect to x is itself a function of x, and may be differentiated in turn. For example, $D_x x^3 = 3x^2$, and $D_x 3x^2 = 6x$.

$D_x[D_x f(x)]$ is written as $D_x{}^2 f(x)$. Differentiating once more gives $D_x{}^3 f(x)$, and so on. Thus, to find $D_x{}^4 x^6$ we have

$$D_x x^6 = 6x^5$$
$$D_x{}^2 x^6 = 30x^4$$
$$D_x{}^3 x^6 = 120x^3$$
$$D_x{}^4 x^6 = 360x^2$$

(We also write $f'(x), f''(x), f'''(x), f^{\text{iv}}(x)$, etc. for $D_x f(x), D_x{}^2 f(x), D_x{}^3 f(x), D_x{}^4 f(x)$, etc.) If we continue with this function, we eventually get 0. In cases such as $1/x$, however, the result is a never-ending string of greater and greater negative powers of x (with certain constant factors). Certain peculiar functions have derivatives at certain points without those derivatives being themselves differentiable. We will avoid such cases here.

To attach some geometrical significance to $D_x^2f(x)$, in terms of the graph of $y=f(x)$, it is recalled that $D_xf(x)$ is the slope of the tangent to the curve, and that a derivative also may be interpreted as a rate of increase. Hence $D_x^2f(x)$ may be thought of as the *rate of increase* (with respect to x) *of the slope of the tangent*. Thus, if $D_x^2f(x)$ is *positive* at a point A, the slope of the tangent *increases* as the point of tangency passes through A (in the direction of x increasing). If $D_x^2f(x)$ is *negative*, the slope decreases. Thus, graphically,

$D_x^2f(x) > 0$: ⟋ if $D_xf(x) > 0$, or: ⟍ if $D_xf(x) < 0$.

$D_x^2f(x) < 0$: ⟋ if $D_xf(x) > 0$, or: ⟍ if $D_xf(x) < 0$.

If $D_x^2f(x) = 0$ then further study is required.

The following example illustrates the usefulness of $D_xf(x)$ and $D_x^2f(x)$ in sketching the graph of $y=f(x)$.

Consider
$$y = x^3 - x,$$
$$D_xy = 3x^2 - 1,$$
$$D_x^2y = 6x,$$
$$y = 0 \text{ at } x = 0, +1, -1,$$
$$D_xy = 0 \text{ at } x = \pm 1/\sqrt{3}.$$

Thus, the curve is horizontal for these values of x. D_xy is clearly negative for values of x between $1/\sqrt{3}$ and $-1/\sqrt{3}$, and positive elsewhere.
$D_x^2y = 0$ at $x = 0$. It is negative when $x < 0$ and positive when $x > 0$.

Putting these considerations together, one is led to the graph shown in Fig 2-4.

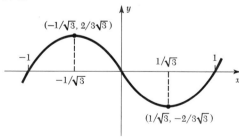

Fig. 2-4

As another example, suppose one wants to find the vertex of the vertical parabola $y = 3x^2 - 12x + 15$ (Fig. 2-5).

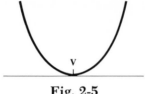

Fig. 2-5

The vertex is at the bottom of the curve, where $D_x y = 0$. This gives $6x - 12 = 0$, hence $x = 2$. Putting $x = 2$ in $3x^2 - 12x + 15$ gives $y = 3$. Hence V is $(2, 3)$.

Exercises

1. Given $y = x^4 - 6x^2$, find:
   (a) the points where $y = 0$,
   (b) the points where $D_x y = 0$,
   (c) the points where $D_x^2 y = 0$.
   Also draw the graph of this equation.

2. Find
   (a) $D_x^2 \ 5x^3$,
   (b) $D_t^3 \ 1/t^2$,
   (c) $D_x^3 \ 12x^2$.

Problems

3. Sketch, without using calculus, the graphs of
   (a) $[x]$,
   (b) $[x]^2$,
   (c) $[|x|]$,
   (d) $\sin [x]$,
   where $[x]$ is the smallest integer greater than x.

2.8 The Chain Rule (the "Function of a Function" Rule)

Frequently the relationship between dependent variables is given indirectly, by means of relationships to other variables. For example, it may be given that $y = \sin x$, where $x = 1/\sqrt{t}$. If $D_x y$ and $D_t x$ are known, is there a simple formula connecting them with $D_t y$?

If one thinks of the interpretation of the derivative as a rate of increase, the answer suggests itself at once. If Y earns money 3 times as fast as X, and X earns money at 2 times the rate of T, then clearly Y earns money at 3×2 times the rate of T. This suggests the formula $D_t y = D_x y \cdot D_t x$. (Whenever this formula is used, it will of course be assumed that y, x, t are related in such a way that the formula makes sense.) Note the resemblance to a cancellation; a similar situation exists in the familiar formula $\log_c a = \log_b a \cdot \log_c b$.

For a proof of this formula, let y, x, t be one set of values of the variables, and $y + \Delta y$, $x + \Delta x$, $t + \Delta t$ another set. The three Δ's will approach zero together.

$$D_t y = \lim_{\Delta t \to 0} \frac{\Delta y}{\Delta t}$$

$$= \lim_{\Delta t \to 0} \frac{\Delta y}{\Delta x} \cdot \frac{\Delta x}{\Delta t}$$

$$= \lim_{\Delta t \to 0} \frac{\Delta y}{\Delta x} \cdot \lim_{\Delta t \to 0} \frac{\Delta x}{\Delta t}$$

$$= \lim_{\Delta x \to 0} \frac{\Delta y}{\Delta x} \cdot \lim_{\Delta t \to 0} \frac{\Delta x}{\Delta t}$$

$$= D_x y \cdot D_t x.$$

(This proof requires more careful treatment with functions whose values oscillate in a certain peculiar way, which will not concern us here.)

This formula, known as the *chain rule*, gives us a method of differentiating functions got by *compounding* functions whose derivatives we already know. To *compound* $f(x)$ and $g(x)$ means to form the function $f[g(x)]$ of x. For example, if $f(x) = \sin x$ and $g(x) = x^2$, then $f[g(x)] = \sin x^2$. Also, $g[f(x)] = (\sin x)^2$. By the chain rule,

$$D_x f[g(x)] = D_{g(x)} f[g(x)] \cdot D_x g(x).$$

Both terms on the right side are known—the second by assumption, and the first because it amounts to $D_t f(t)$ [where t is $g(x)$], which is also known by assumption.

As an example, consider $D_x (x^2 + 3x)^{51}$. Expanding $(x^2 + 3x)^{51}$ and then differentiating the resultant sum would yield the answer, but at great labor. The chain rule reduces the work to

$$D_x (x^2 + 3x)^{51} = D_{(x^2 + 3x)}(x^2 + 3x)^{51} \cdot D_x(x^2 + 3x)$$
$$= 51(x^2 + 3x)^{50} \cdot (2x + 3).$$

It should be noted that functions may not be compoundable if the values of one lie outside the range over which the other is defined. For example, if $f(x) = -x^4$ and $g(x) = \sqrt{x}$, then $f[g(x)] = -(\sqrt{x})^4$, but the attempt to provide $g[f(x)]$ leads to $\sqrt{-x^4}$, which does not exist within the realm of real numbers.

Exercises

1. Find:
   (a) $D_x (2x - 5x^3)^{21}$,

   (c) $D_y \left[\dfrac{2y + 9}{1 - y^2}\right]$,

   (b) $D_t 1/(1 + t^2)^9$,

   (d) $D_{2x+4} (x^3 + 2x^2)$.

2.9 Inverse Functions

If $y = f(x)$ and $x = g(y)$, then f and g are said to be *inverses* of one another. For example, the square and the square root are inverses, as are sin and sin $^{-1}$. (See Section 2.12.)

What connection is there between $D_x y$ and $D_y x$? By the chain rule,

$$D_x y \cdot D_y x = D_y y = 1.$$

Hence

$$D_x y = \frac{1}{D_y x}.$$

The notion of the inverse of a function, $f(x)$, is uncomplicated in such a case as $f(x) = 2x - 4$. This function is defined for all values of x, and for every y there is exactly one x such that $y = 2x - 4$. In fact, $y = 2x - 4$ if and only if $x = (4 + y)/2$, so that the functions associated with the expressions $2x - 4$ and $(4 + y)/2$ are inverses of one another.

If $f(x) = 2x - 4$ and $g(x) = (4 + x)/2$ then we have, without any qualifications, the fundamental result

$$f[g(x)] = g[f(x)] = x.$$

If, however, $f(x)$ takes some values more than once, then the situation becomes more complicated. Consider, for example, $f(x) = x^2$. This takes the value 0 exactly once, namely when $x = 0$, but it takes the value 4 twice, namely when $x = 2$ and when $x = -2$, and similarly for every positive value. It is never negative.

Thus, if we try to solve $y = x^2$ to get $x = g(y)$ for some single-valued function g, we fail, for each value of y yields two, one, or no values for x, depending on the value of y (Fig. 2-6).

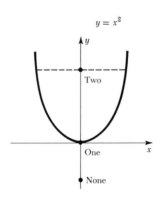

Fig. 2-6

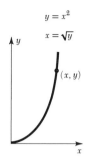

Fig. 2-7

The nearest thing to an inverse is got by using only the first-quadrant portion of the graph of $y = x^2$. In Fig. 2-7, y attains the value x^2 only once—where $x = \sqrt{y}$ (the positive square root of y). Thus we often refer to the functions associated with x^2 and $\sqrt{y}$ as "inverses" of one another. However, there are two complications in this case: (1) $\sqrt{x}$ is defined only for $x \geqq 0$, and (2) if $f(x) = x^2$ and $g(x) = \sqrt{x}$, then, although $f[g(x)] = (\sqrt{x})^2 = x$, we have

$$g[f(x)] = \sqrt{x^2} = + x \text{ or } - x,$$

depending on whether x is positive or negative.

In general, when a function fails to have an inverse (in the strict, uncomplicated sense) we can often get a useful "inverse" out of it by using only part of its graph, but we must then take into account complications such as (1) and (2) above.

2.10 The Derivative of x^n (for n a Rational Number)

The chain rule enables us to differentiate $x^{r/s}$, where r and s are any integers (s not zero). Let $y = x^{r/s}$; then $y^s = x^r$. Differentiating both sides with respect to x gives

$$D_x y^s = D_x x^r$$
$$D_y y^s \cdot D_x y = rx^{r-1} \qquad \text{(applying the chain rule on the left side)}$$
$$sy^{s-1} D_x y = rx^{r-1}$$
$$D_x y = \frac{r}{s} \frac{x^{r-1}}{y^{s-1}}$$
$$= \frac{r}{s} x^{(r/s-1)} \qquad \text{(substituting for } y\text{)}$$
$$= nx^{n-1}.$$

Exercises

1. Find:
   (a) $D_x x^{2/3}$,
   (b) $D_x x^{7/5}$,
   (c) $D_z z^{-4/3}$,
   (d) $D_u \sqrt{u}$,
   (e) $D_x (1+\sqrt{x})^{1/3}$ (use the chain rule first).

2.11 Trigonometric Functions

If the derivative of one trigonometric function of x is known, then the derivatives of the others can be found, since they are all expressible in terms of any one, by means of square roots and arithmetical operations.

We begin with $\sin x$.

$$
\begin{aligned}
D_x \sin x &= \lim_{h\to 0} \frac{\sin (x+h) - \sin x}{h} \\
&= \lim_{h\to 0} \frac{2 \cos (x+h/2) \sin h/2}{h} \\
&= \lim_{h\to 0} \cos (x+h/2) \cdot \frac{\sin h/2}{h/2} \\
&= \cos x \cdot 1 \quad [\text{See Section 1.8, (iii)}].
\end{aligned}
$$

This is not surprising if one thinks of the graph of the sine function, with slope oscillating between $+1$ and -1, and the slope being zero at $90°$, $270°$, etc., where $\cos x$ is zero (Fig. 2-8).

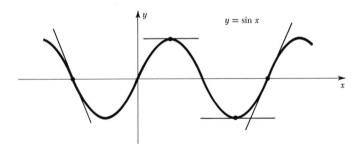

Fig. 2-8

The neatest way to find $D_x \cos x$ is as follows:

$$
\begin{aligned}
D_x \cos x &= D_x \sin (\pi/2 - x) \\
&= \cos (\pi/2 - x) \cdot (-1) \\
&= -\sin x.
\end{aligned}
$$

Furthermore,

$$D_x \tan x = D_x \frac{\sin x}{\cos x}$$

$$= \frac{\cos x \cdot \cos x - \sin x \, (-\sin x)}{\cos^2 x}$$

$$= \frac{1}{\cos^2 x}$$

$$= \sec^2 x$$

$$= 1 + \tan^2 x \qquad \text{(also a useful form.)}$$

Derivatives of other trigonometric functions of x can now be found quite easily.

2.12 Inverse Trigonometric Functions

If y is positive, then there are two numbers whose square is y. One of them—the positive one—we denote by $\sqrt{y}$, and call it the principal square root of y.

A similar thing is done in the case of a trigonometric function (Fig. 2-9).

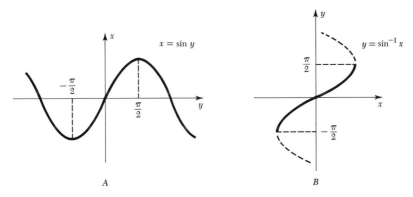

Fig. 2-9

There are infinitely many numbers whose sine is x, as is readily seen from graph B, got by reflecting graph A in the line $y = x$. The one which lies between and including $-\pi/2$ and $+\pi/2$ is denoted by "$\sin^{-1} x$" and called the "inverse sine," or "arc sine," of x. This amounts to using only the solid part of the graph in B.

If

$$y = \sin^{-1} x, \qquad \text{then} \quad x = \sin y.$$

$$D_x y = \frac{1}{D_y x}$$

$$= \frac{1}{\cos y}$$

$$= \frac{1}{\pm\sqrt{1 - \sin^2 y}} \qquad \text{(which sign?)}.$$

Since y is defined to be between and to include $-\pi/2$ and $+\pi/2$, $\cos y$ must be positive. Hence "+" is wanted. Continuing,

$$D_x \sin^{-1} x = \frac{1}{\sqrt{1 - \sin^2 y}}$$

$$= \frac{1}{\sqrt{1 - x^2}}$$

(see Fig. 2-10).

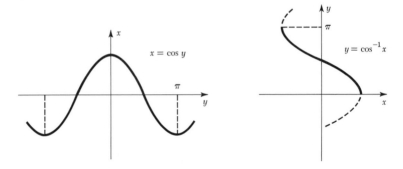

Fig. 2-10

Similarly, we take $\cos^{-1} x$ to lie between and to include 0 and π, and we get (see Fig. 2-11)

$$D_x \cos^{-1} x = \frac{1}{D_y x}$$

$$= \frac{1}{-\sin y}$$

$$= \frac{-1}{\sqrt{1 - x^2}}.$$

$\text{Tan}^{-1} x$ lies between $-\pi/2$ and $+\pi/2$, and $D_x \tan^{-1} x = 1/(1 + x^2)$ (proof left to reader).

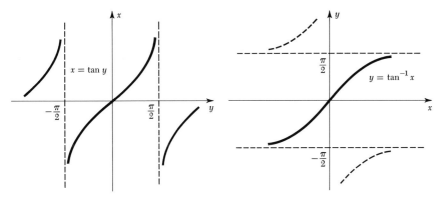

Fig. 2-11

Exercises

1. Differentiate with respect to x:

   (a) $(x^2 + 3x)^{17}$,

   (c) $\dfrac{1}{(x^2 + 9x)^{72}}$,

   (e) $\tan(1 + x^2)$,

   (g) $(\sin x + \tan 2x)^{95}$,

   (i) $\sin(\cos x)$,

   (k) $\sin^{-1} x^2$,

   (b) $(1 + 9x^3)^{257}$,

   (d) $\sin 3x$,

   (f) $\cos \sqrt{x} + 4 \sin x^2$,

   (h) $\cos \dfrac{x^5 + 2x}{1 - x}$,

   (j) $\tan^{-1}(1 + x)$,

   (l) $(1 + \cos^{-1} x)^{92}$.

Problems

2. Find the angle at which the graphs of $\sin x$ and $\cos x$ intersect.

3. Derive formulas for $D_x \sin x^\circ$, $D_x \cos x^\circ$, $D_x \tan x^\circ$ ($^\circ$ referring to degrees).

4. Derive formulas for the derivatives of the remaining trigonometric functions and their inverses. ($\sec^{-1} x$ is taken between 0 and $\pi/2$ for x positive, and between $-\pi$ and $-\pi/2$ for x negative. $\csc^{-1} x$ is taken between 0 and $\pi/2$, and $-\pi$ and $-\pi/2$. $\cot^{-1} x$ is taken between 0 and π.)

5. (a) Prove the formulas for $D_x \cos x$, $D_x \tan x$ directly from the definition of the derivative.

   (b) Prove the formula for $D_x \cos x$ from that for $D_x \sin x$, using the identity $\cos x = \pm\sqrt{1 - \sin^2 x}$.

6. Find $\lim\limits_{x \to 0} \dfrac{\sin 2x}{x}$.

7. Draw on one set of axes the graphs of $\sin x$, $\sin^2 x$.

2.13 Logarithmic and Exponential Functions: The Number *e*

When *a* is positive, we may form the *exponential function* a^x. For $a > 1$ (the most commonly used case), its graph is shown in Fig. 2-12.

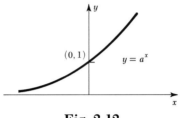

Fig. 2-12

The graph is asymptotic to the *x*-axis and rises steadily. The function attains only positive values, but every positive value is attained exactly once. Thus the function has an inverse, defined for all positive values of *x*: this inverse is called the *logarithm of x to base a* and is written $\log_a x$.

Its graph is obtained by reflecting the above graph in the line $y = x$. It is asymptotic to the negative *y*-axis and rises steadily (Fig. 2-13).

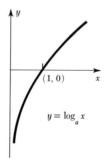

Fig. 2-13

We will assume that the reader is familiar with the basic algebraic properties of a^x and $\log_a x$.

$$D_x \log_a x = \lim_{h \to 0} \frac{\log_a (x+h) - \log_a x}{h}$$

$$= \lim_{h \to 0} \frac{\log_a [(x+h)/x]}{h}$$

$$= \lim_{h \to 0} \frac{\log_a (1 + h/x)}{h}$$

$$= \lim_{h \to 0} \frac{1}{x} \frac{\log_a (1 + h/x)}{h/x} \qquad \text{(this step makes the terms in } h \text{ alike, and easier to deal with)}$$

$$= \lim_{h \to 0} 1/x \log_a (1 + h/x)^{x/h}.$$

Denoting x/h by "n" [n tends to infinity ($n \to \infty$) as h approaches 0], we have

$$\lim_{n \to \infty} 1/x \log_a (1 + 1/n)^n$$
$$= 1/x \lim_{n \to \infty} \log_a (1 + 1/n)^n$$
$$= 1/x \log_a \lim_{n \to \infty} (1 + 1/n)^n.$$

Here we use the fact (which we assume to be intuitively plausible but which can be proved) that as a quantity a approaches a limit A, its logarithm $\log a$ approaches the limit $\log A$. (This amounts to the fact that if a is very nearly equal to A, then $\log a$ is very nearly equal to $\log A$.) Thus the limit of a logarithm is equal to the logarithm of the limit.

Actual computation for very large values of n gives values of $(1 + 1/n)^n$ very close to a certain number, 2.71828 .... One expects $(1 + 1/n)^n$ to approach a definite limit, since the derivative we are evaluating is equal to the slope of the tangent to the curve $y = \log_a x$ at an arbitrary point (x, y) on it, and this presumably exists and is finite. (See Problem 3 at the end of this section.)

This number, $\lim_{n \to \infty} (1 + 1/n)^n$, is denoted by "$e$." Our formula thus becomes

$$D_x \log_a x = 1/x \log_a e.$$

So far, a has been an arbitrary positive number other than 1. This formula suggests that it would be convenient to use $a = e$, for this gives

$$D_x \log_e x = 1/x \log_e e$$
$$= 1/x.$$

For this reason, and others arising out of it, it is customary in theoretical mathematics generally to use logarithms to base e.

$\log_e x$ will henceforth be denoted by "ln x." ("log x" is also a common notation.)

Thus $$D_x \ln x = \frac{1}{x}.$$

If $x = \ln y$, then $y = e^x$—the inverse of $\ln x$.

$$D_x y = \frac{1}{D_y x}$$
$$= \frac{1}{1/y}$$
$$= y$$
$$= e^x.$$

Thus $De^x = e^x$.

Thus we get the remarkable result that e^x is equal to its own derivative. This is true also of ce^x, c being any constant.

To differentiate functions of x such as 2^x, $\log_{10} x$, etc., we convert to base e by using algebraic identities and then proceed as above.

Thus, to find $D_x 2^x$, first note that $2 = e^{\ln 2}$, since $\ln 2$ means $\log_e 2$, which is by definition the power of e that gives 2, and raising e to the power that gives 2 obviously gives 2.

2^x then becomes $(e^{\ln 2})^x$, which is $e^{\ln 2 \cdot x}$. We then have

$$D_x 2^x = D_x e^{\ln 2 \cdot x}$$
$$= \ln 2\, e^{\ln 2 \cdot x}$$
$$= \ln 2 \cdot 2^x.$$

An alternative procedure is to write $y = 2^x$ and then take logarithms before differentiating. This gives

$$\ln y = \ln 2^x,$$
$$\ln y = x\ln 2,$$
$$\frac{1}{y} D_x y = \ln 2,$$
$$D_x y = \ln 2 \cdot y$$
$$= \ln 2 \cdot 2^x.$$

To find $D_x \log_{10} x$ note that $\log_{10} x = \log_e x \cdot \log_{10} e$. (More generally, $\log_c a = \log_b a \cdot \log_c b$.) The remainder is left as an exercise.

A function of x such as x^x, which combines the features of both a power function and an exponential function, can also be dealt with in this way:

$x^x = e^{(\ln x) \cdot x}$, and the right side can be differentiated in the normal way.

The appearance of the number e on the mathematical scene is less mysterious if one understands its role as a natural *unit of growth*. Suppose a cell performs the division process in one second. After 1, 2, 3, 4, ... seconds there are 2, 4, 8, 16, ... cells—that is, 2^1, 2^2, 2^3, 2^4, ... cells. After n seconds there are 2^n cells. Thus, growth of this kind is exponential.

Now suppose a unit mass grows, by division, every $1/n$ seconds. If the growth per unit is K units per $1/n$ second, then $K=1/n$, if the average rate is to be unity.

The amounts present at successive instants are shown in Fig. 2-14.

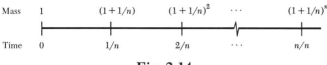

Fig. 2-14

If larger and larger values of n are taken, the little intervals of time become smaller and smaller, and the growth approaches *continuous* (smooth) *growth*; then we get that: If a *unit* mass grows *continuously* at unit rate for *unit* period it becomes $\lim_{n\to\infty} (1+1/n)^n$ units—that is, e units.

This connection with the exponential process of growth makes the appearance of e in differentiating exponentials and logarithms not too surprising.

The formula $D_x \ln x = 1/x$ has a striking feature shared by the formulas involving the inverse trigonometric functions. The function of x, $\ln x$, and its derivative with respect to x, $1/x$, belong to different "species"—the latter being a simple rational function of x. Thus, the process of differentiation can lead outside the "family" of functions being differentiated. It is also noteworthy that $1/x$ is a missing power of x not appearing as a derivative of $K \cdot x^n$ for any n.

Exercises

1. Differentiate with respect to x:

   (a) e^{2x},

   (b) $e^{(x^2)}$,

   (c) $2x + e^{\sqrt{x}}$,

   (d) $1/e^{9x}$,

   (e) $\cos(e^{-x})$,

   (f) $\dfrac{e^x + e^{-x}}{2}$,

   (g) $\dfrac{e^x - e^{-x}}{2}$,

   (h) $\ln(1+x)$,

   (i) $x \ln(1/x)$,

   (j) $\ln e^x$,

   (k) $\ln[x + x \sin (1/x)]$,

   (l) $e^{2x} + \tan x$,

   (m) $(4e^{-x} + 1)^{10}$.

2. Differentiate with respect to x:

   (a) $\sin (1/x)$,

   (b) $\sin^{-1} x + \cos^{-1} x$,

   (c) $e^{\cos 2x}$,

   (d) 4^x,

   (e) $3\sqrt{x}$,

   (f) $\log_{10} (\ln x)$,

   (g) $\dfrac{3 \cos x + 5x^2}{1 + \sqrt{x}}$,

   (h) $1/\ln x$,

(i) $e^{(e^x)}$,

(j) $\dfrac{x^{-3/4}+4x^{1/4}}{(x+1)^2}$,

(k) $\tan^{-1}(1/\sin x)$,

(l) $\sin^{-1}(\sin x)$,

(m) $(x^0+x^1+x^2+x^3)^4$,

(n) $e^{2\sqrt{x}}$,

(o) $(1+\tan x)^{\sin x}$,

(p) $\ln/x - 1/2 \ln x$,

(q) $\sin(4/3)$,

(r) $2/\tan x$,

(s) $\dfrac{1}{e^{1/x}}$,

(t) $\sqrt{1-2^x}$,

(u) $\dfrac{1}{\sqrt{1-2^x}}$.

Problems

3. (a) Expand $(1+1/n)^n$ by the binomial expansion, and show that it increases in value as n increases. (*Hint:* show that each term increases and that the number of terms increases.)

   (b) Prove that $(1+1/n)^n$ is always less than 3. (*Hint:* find a G.P. whose terms are all greater than those of the above expansion to which they correspond.)

4. Prove the general product-quotient rule

$$\left[\frac{u_1 u_2 \cdots u_n}{v_1 v_2 \cdots v_m}\right] = \left[\frac{u_1 u_2 \cdots u_n}{v_1 v_2 \cdots v_m}\right]\left[\frac{u_1'}{u_1}+\cdots+\frac{u_n'}{u_n}-\frac{v_1'}{v_1}-\cdots-\frac{v_m'}{v_m}\right].$$

   (*Hint:* take logarithms.)

5. Find the derivatives with respect to x of:

   (a) $x^{(x^x)}$,

   (b) $\log_x a$,

   (c) $(\sin x)^{\cos x}$,

   (d) $(1+\tan x)^{\sin x}$.

2.14 The Derivative of x^n (General)

We can now prove that $D_x x^n = n x^{n-1}$ for arbitrary n. Let $y=x^n$.

$$\ln y = n \ln x,$$

$$\frac{1}{y}D_x y = n \cdot \frac{1}{x},$$

$$D_x y = y \cdot n \cdot \frac{1}{x},$$

$$= n x^{n-1}.$$

2.15 Functions Defined Parametrically

The relation between two variables, x and y, is not always given by one equation in x and y. Frequently they are connected via a third variable, say t, known as a *parameter*. Thus, one may be given

$$x = f(t), \qquad y = g(t).$$

In such a case, the chain rule provides a ready means of finding D_xy, for $D_ty = D_xy\, D_tx$, and hence

$$D_xy = \frac{D_ty}{D_tx}.$$

It is often convenient to omit the subscript "t", getting

$$D_xy = \frac{Dy}{Dx}.$$

One can also write $Dy = D_xy\, Dx$, etc., when it is clearly understood that a parameter is involved, and that the differentiation is with respect to this parameter. Note that in these formulas it doesn't actually matter which variable one has in mind as parameter; the results will always be valid (assuming, of course, that the parameter is a variable related to x and y in such a way that the results make sense). Furthermore, one can always assume, trivially, that x and y are connected parametrically—for example, with x itself as parameter, in which case Dy is D_xy, and Dx is 1. Our use of this notation will be postponed until later. (It is more customary to use "d" rather than "D," giving "dy/dx"; presentations of this notation—the "differential" notation—vary considerably, and not infrequently involve complications that will not arise here.)

$D_x{}^2y$ can be calculated by applying the same rule to D_xy, which has just been found. Thus

$$D_x{}^2y = D_x\,(D_xy) = \frac{D_t\,(D_xy)}{D_tx}.$$

(On replacing D_xy in the numerator by D_ty/D_tx, we get the notation d^2y/dx^2.) The results are similar for derivatives of higher order. As an example, suppose $x = e^t$, $y = t^3$.

Then
$$D_xy = \frac{D_ty}{D_tx}$$
$$= \frac{3t^2}{e^t},$$

and
$$D_x{}^2y = \frac{D_t\,(3t^2/e^t)}{D_tx} = \frac{6t - 3t^2}{e^{2t}}.$$

We observe that the result, just like x and y, appears as a function of t.

2.16 Functions Defined Implicitly

When x and y are connected by a single equation, it need not be of the form $y = f(x)$. Often it is in a form such as $x^2 + xy^3 + y^2 = 3$.

Here we might think of solving for y in terms of x, but it is not necessary (in fact it may be not only difficult but impossible) to do this in order to find $D_x y$. Instead we note that the equation defines, implicitly, y as a function of x, and we differentiate both sides with respect to x as they stand, keeping this in mind. This gives

$$2x + x3y^2 \, D_x y + y^3 + 2yD_x y = 0. \tag{1}$$

Hence
$$D_x y = \frac{-2x - y^3}{3xy^2 + 2y}. \tag{2}$$

To find $D_x{}^2 y$, we differentiate (1) [or (2)], getting

$$2 + x3y^2 D_x{}^2 y + (x6yD_x y + 3y^2) \, D_x y + 3y^2 D_x y + 2yD_x{}^2 y + 2D_x yD_x y = 0.$$

Substituting for $D_x y$ from (2), we then solve for $D_x{}^2 y$. We solve similarly for higher order derivatives.

For another example, consider

$$xy + 3 = 0,$$

$$xD_x y + y = 0,$$

hence
$$D_x y = -\frac{y}{x}.$$

$$xD_x{}^2 y + D_x y + D_x y = 0,$$

hence
$$D_x{}^2 y = \frac{-2D_x y}{x} = \frac{+2y}{x^2}.$$

$$xD_x{}^3 y + D_x{}^2 y + 2D_x{}^2 y = 0,$$

hence
$$D_x{}^3 y = \frac{-3D_x{}^2 y}{x} = \frac{-6y}{x^3}.$$

Exercises

1. If y is the function of x defined implicitly by the equation
$$x^2 + xy + y^3 - 1 = 0,$$
find the values of $D_x y$, $D_x{}^2 y$ at the point $(0,1)$.

2. (a) Given $x^2/a^2 + y^2/b^2 = 1$, find $D_x y$, $D_x{}^2 y$ when $x = a/2$.
   (b) Given $x^{2/3} + y^{2/3} = a^{2/3}$, find $D_x y$, $D_x{}^2 y$ when $x = a/2$.

3. Find $D_x y$, $D_x{}^2 y$ at $(0,0)$ in each of the following cases:
   (a) $x = a(\theta - \sin \theta)$, $y = a(1 - \cos \theta)$.
   (b) $x = \sin 2\theta$, $y = \cos \theta$.
   (c) $x = \dfrac{3t}{1 + t^3}$, $y = \dfrac{3t^2}{1 + t^3}$.

2.17 Summary of the Chapter

The notions of speed and of the slope of the tangent to a curve were seen to be instances of the mathematical concept of the derivative: by the derivative of $f(x)$ with respect to x is meant

$$\lim_{h \to 0} \frac{f(x+h) - f(x)}{h},$$

denoted by $D_x f(x)$, or $f'(x)$.

The problem at once arises of being able to differentiate the functions of x we are familiar with. These are all combinations of a rather small family of functions of x. Their differentiation amounts to the application of the formulas given by the following table. (The first group tells what to do with given combinations of functions with known derivatives; the second gives the derivatives of the basic functions out of which more complicated ones are constructed.)

$f(x)$	$D_x f(x) = f'(x)$
$r(x) \pm s(x)$	$r'(x) \pm s'(x)$
$r(x) \cdot s(x)$	$r(x) \cdot s'(x) + r'(x) \cdot s(x)$
$\dfrac{r(x)}{s(x)}$	$\dfrac{s(x) \cdot r'(x) - r(x) \cdot s'(x)}{[s(x)]^2}$
$K \cdot r(x)$	$K \cdot r'(x)$
$F[r(x)]$	$D_{r(x)} F[r(x)] \cdot D_x r(x)$
K (any constant)	0
x^n	nx^{n-1}
$\sin x$	$\cos x$
$\cos x$	$-\sin x$
$\tan x$	$1 + \tan^2 x$
$\sin^{-1} x$	$\dfrac{1}{\sqrt{1-x^2}}$
$\cos^{-1} x$	$\dfrac{-1}{\sqrt{1-x^2}}$
$\tan^{-1} x$	$\dfrac{1}{1+x^2}$
$\ln x$	$\dfrac{1}{x}$
e^x	e^x

It was seen that a function of x need not be known explicitly in order to find its derivative.

3

Applications of Differentiation

Having developed an effective technique of differentiation, we are now able to turn to a variety of applications.

3.1 Rates of Change

By the *rate of change* of one variable, y, with respect to another, x, we mean $D_x y$. To compute rates of change we usually first express y as a function of x (possibly implicitly, or parametrically), and then, using our differentiation formulas, find $D_x y$. A few examples will show how this is done.

(i)   A particle oscillates back and forth along the x-axis according to the equation $x = \sin t$, where "t" denotes time, and "x" the co-ordinate of the particle (Fig. 3-1).

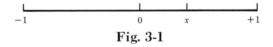

$$\begin{array}{ccc} -1 & \quad 0 \quad & x \qquad +1 \end{array}$$

Fig. 3-1

What are its velocity and acceleration as functions of time? In particular, what are they when $t = \pi/2$ and when $t = 0$?

Since velocity is rate of change of distance with respect to time, and acceleration is rate of change of velocity with respect to time, we have:

$$\text{Velocity,} \quad v = D_t x = \cos t,$$
$$\text{Acceleration,} \quad a = D_t v = -\sin t.$$

38

When $t = \pi/2$ we have $v = 0$, $a = -1$. When $t = 0$ we have $v = 1$, $a = 0$.

(ii) What is the rate of change of the area of a circle with respect to its radius?

$$\text{Area,} \quad A = \pi r^2,$$

hence $D_r A = 2\pi r$. We note that this is the circumference.

A similar result holds in the case of a sphere, for $D_r\, 4/3\ \pi r^3 = 4\pi r^2$, which is the surface area.

(iii) A kite 300 feet in the air is moving horizontally away from its base on the ground at a velocity of 20 f.p.s. How fast is the string unwinding when 500 feet of string are out? (See Fig. 3-2.)

Let s, x be as shown: $s = \sqrt{(300)^2 + x^2}$, and $D_t x = 20$, also $x = 400$ when $s = 500$.

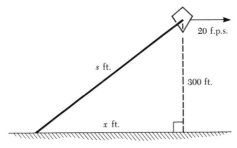

Fig. 3-2

The required rate is $D_t s$, when $s = 500$.

$$D_t s = D_x s \cdot D_t x$$
$$= \frac{1}{2}\, (300^2 + x^2)^{-1/2}\ 2x \cdot 20$$
$$= \frac{400 \cdot 20}{500} \quad \text{when } s = 500$$
$$= 16.$$

Hence the string is unwinding at 16 f.p.s. at the given instant.

An alternative procedure is to work directly from the equation $s^2 = x^2 + 300^2$, without solving for s. This gives, on differentiating with respect to t,

$$2s \cdot D_t s = 2x D_t x.$$

Hence,
$$D_t s = \frac{x}{s}\, D_t x$$
$$= \frac{400}{500} \cdot 20 \quad \text{when } s = 500$$
$$= 16.$$

Exercises

1. A point moves along the curve $y = \cos x$, its x-coordinate increasing at a steady rate of 1 unit per second. How fast is it rising when $x = \pi/4$? $x = \pi/2$? $x = 3\pi/2$? Show that its vertical acceleration is proportional to its distance from the x-axis.

2. x and y are related by the equation $x^2 - 2xy + y^2 - 1 = 0$. If x is changing at a rate of k units per second, how fast is y changing at the instant when $x = 2$ and $y = 3$?

3. Given $x = \sin u$, $y = e^u$, $x = 3t^2$, find $D_t y$ when $u = \pi/2$.

4. A man fishes from a bridge 10 feet high. He hooks a fish which swims directly downstream at 15 m.p.h. How fast is the line unreeling when the fish is 40 feet away (horizontally)?

5. The sides of a rectangle are 8 and 6 inches. The longer side is increasing at a rate of 2 inches per second, and the shorter side is decreasing at a rate of 4 inches per second. Is the area increasing or decreasing, and how fast?

6. Find the rate of change of the area of a square with respect to the length of a side at the instant when the length of the side is 10 ft.

7. Find the rate of change of the volume of a sphere with respect to its diameter at the instant when the diameter is 24 ft.

8. A right circular cylinder has fixed height h. Find the rate of change of its volume with respect to the diameter of its circular section at the instant when this diameter is K.

Problems

9. A ladder 20 feet long leaning against a vertical wall begins to slip. A man stands 5 feet from the top of the ladder. How fast is he falling (consider vertical components only) if the bottom of the ladder is 10 feet from the wall and is sliding outwards at 4 feet per second? Assuming the latter rate to be maintained, discuss his rate of fall generally.

10. A revolving light, 5 miles away from a straight shore, revolves once every 5 minutes. A point P is on the shore, 13 miles from the light. At what speed does the spot of light pass P in moving along the shore?

11. A ship is sailing west at 8 m.p.h. Another ship, 12 miles north of it, is sailing north at 6 m.p.h. How fast was the distance between the ships changing one hour ago?

12. A spherical balloon is being filled with gas at a rate of 100 cubic feet per minute.

(a) What is the rate of increase of the surface area at the instant when the radius is 6 feet?
(b) How fast is the radius increasing at this instant?

3.2 Tangents and Normals to Curves

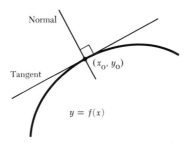

Fig. 3-3

Given a curve $y=f(x)$ and a point (x_0, y_0) on it (Fig. 3-3) we have seen that the slope of the tangent at (x_0, y_0) is the value of $D_x f(x)$ at that point—that is, $f'(x_0)$. Hence the equation of the tangent is

$$y - y_0 = f'(x_0)(x - x_0)$$

and the equation of the normal is

$$y - y_0 = -\frac{1}{f'(x_0)}(x - x_0).$$

Examples

(i) It is not necessary to exhibit y explicitly as a function of x. For example, consider the circle $x^2 + y^2 = a^2$ (Fig. 3-4).

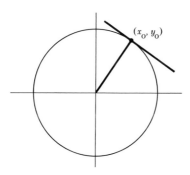

Fig. 3-4

Using the methods of Section 2.17 we get $2x + 2y\, D_x y = 0$.

Hence,
$$D_x y = -\frac{x}{y}$$
$$= -\frac{x_0}{y_0} \quad \text{at } (x_0, y_0).$$

Thus the equations of the tangent and normal are, respectively,

$$y - y_0 = -\frac{x_0}{y_0}(x - x_0)$$

and

$$y - y_0 = \frac{y_0}{x_0}(x - x_0).$$

The equation of the tangent simplifies as follows:

$$yy_0 - y_0^2 = -xx_0 + x_0^2,$$
$$xx_0 + yy_0 = x_0^2 + y_0^2,$$
$$xx_0 + yy_0 = a^2.$$

The equation of the normal is

$$x_0 y - x_0 y_0 = x y_0 - x_0 y_0,$$
$$y = \frac{y_0}{x_0} x.$$

This is the equation of a straight line passing through the center $(0,0)$ of the circle.

(ii) To find the equations of the tangent and normal to $y = x^3 + 2x^2 + 4$ at the point where $x = 1$, we first note, by direct substitution, that when $x = 1$ we have $y = 7$. Next we differentiate the given equation, getting

$$y' = 3x^2 + 4x,$$

which is equal to 7 when x is 1. Thus the required tangent contains $(1,7)$ and has slope equal to 7. Its equation is therefore $y - 7 = 7(x - 1)$; that is, $7x - y = 0$. The normal has slope $-1/7$; hence its equation is $y - 7 = -1/7\ (x - 1)$; that is, $x + 7y - 50 = 0$.

Exercises

1. Prove that the tangent to $y = x^2$ at $(2,4)$ passes through the point $(1,0)$. Where does the normal at the same point meet the y-axis?

2. Find the equations of the tangents and normals to the locus of (x,y) in the following cases:

(a) $x^2 + 4y^2 = 20$ at $(4,1)$,
(b) $x^3 + 3xy + y^3 = 15$ at $(1,2)$,
(c) $x = 1/(1-t)$, $y = 2t^3$ at $t = 0$,
(d) $x = \sin 2\theta$, $y = \theta + \cos 2\theta$ at $\theta = \pi/2$.

Problems

3. (a) Show that the equation of the tangent to the parabola $y^2 = 4px$ at a point (x_0, y_0) on it is $yy_0 = 2p(x + x_0)$.
   (b) How many normals pass through a given point (a, O)? Discuss how the answer depends on the value of a, and illustrate graphically.

4. Prove that tangents to a parabola which are perpendicular to each other always meet on the directrix of the parabola.

5. (a)

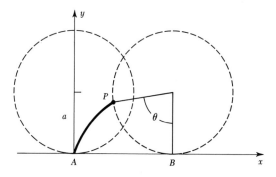

Fig. 3-5

A circle of radius a rolls, without slipping, on a straight line. Using axes located as shown in Fig. 3-5, prove that the locus of a point $P(x,y)$ on the circumference of the circle has equations $x = a\theta - a \sin \theta$, $y = a - a \cos \theta$.
(*Hint:* length of segment AB = length of arc PB.)
   (b) Sketch the locus described above (a *cycloid*).
   (c) Prove that the tangent to the cycloid at P is always perpendicular to PB (B being the point of contact with the circle).

6. Prove that the curves $x^2 - 2px + y^2 = 0$, $x^2 - 2qy + y^2 = 0$ intersect at right angles.

7. Show that the length cut off on the tangent to $x^{2/3} + y^{2/3} = a^{2/3}$ by the x and y axes is constant.

8. Show that the sum of the intercepts of the tangent to $x^{1/2} + y^{1/2} = a^{1/2}$ is a constant, independent of where the tangent is drawn.

3.3 Sketching Graphs

As a rule it is not necessary to have a very accurate graph of a function. All we need to know are the main features, such as whether it is increasing or decreasing, or whether the curve curls upward or downward, at a given point. These features in most cases can be easily seen by inspection of the values of the first and second derivatives involved.

Since $D_x f(x)$ can be interpreted as the slope of the graph of $y = f(x)$, and $D_x^2 f(x)$ is the rate of increase of this slope with respect to x, the curve will appear as drawn in the following cases:

$D_x f(x) > 0$, slope > 0

and
$D_x^2 f(x) > 0$, slope increasing
    (as x increases)

$D_x f(x) > 0$, slope > 0

and
$D_x^2 f(x) < 0$, slope decreasing

$D_x f(x) < 0$, slope < 0

and
$D_x^2 f(x) > 0$, slope increasing

$D_x f(x) < 0$, slope < 0

and
$D_x^2 f(x) < 0$, slope decreasing

$D_x f(x) = 0$ indicates a horizontal tangent, as in:

(a)

(b)

$D_x^2 f(x) \leq 0,$ $D_x^2 f(x) \geq 0,$

(c)    or (d)

$$D_x{}^2f(x) = 0, \qquad\qquad\qquad\qquad D_x{}^2f(x) = 0.$$

In (a) we have a *maximum* point, in (b) a *minimum* point, and in (c) and (d) neither, even though $D_x{}^2f(x) = 0$. If $D_x{}^2f(x) < 0$ at P [assuming $D_xf(x) = 0$], then we definitely have case (a), and if $D_x{}^2f(x) > 0$, then we have case (b). If $D_x{}^2f(x) = 0$, then we can distinguish the four cases as follows:

(a) $D_xf(x) > 0$ immediately to the left of P and < 0 to the right of P.

(b) $D_xf(x) < 0$ immediately to the left of P and > 0 to the right of P.

(c) $D_xf(x) \geqslant 0$ throughout.

(d) $D_xf(x) \leqslant 0$ throughout.

A point P at which $D_x{}^2f(x) = 0$ and at which there is a change in sign of $D_x{}^2f(x)$ as the point concerned passes through P is called a *point of inflection* [$D_xf(x)$ need not be 0]. At such a point the curve crosses its tangent.

An example is the graph of $y = x^3 + x$ (Fig. 3-6). Here $y' = 3x^2 + 1$ and $y'' = 6x$. At $x = 0$ we have $y'' = 0$, and y'' changes in sign as x passes through the value 0, hence there is a point of inflection at $(0,0)$. The slope at $(0,0)$ is 1.

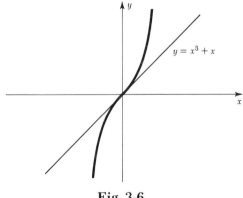

Fig. 3-6

Example

Let us sketch the graph of $y = x^4 + 2x^3$. First we find some points on the curve by finding where it meets the x-axis. This will be where

$y=0$, hence where $x^4+2x^3=0$; that is, $x^3(x+2)=0$. This yields $x=0$ (a triple root, hence something special should happen at this point) and $x=-2$. Next we see what the curve is doing at these points, using $D_x y=4x^3+6x^2$ and $D_x{}^2 y=12x^2+12x$.

At $x=0$, $D_x y=0$, hence we have a horizontal tangent. Since $D_x{}^2 y=0$ we must investigate the sign of $D_x y$ near $P(0,0)$ in order to tell which of cases (a), (b), (c), or (d) holds. For x near to 0, $6x^2$ is greater in absolute value than $4x^3$; hence $D_x y$ is $\geqslant 0$ near P, and we have case (c) at $x=0$. At $x=-2$, $D_x y=-8$ and $D_x{}^2 y>0$.

Putting these bits of information together, we get the partial graph shown in Fig. 3-7.

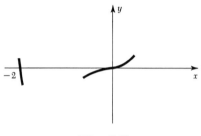

Fig. 3-7

To get all points where $D_x y=0$ we solve $4x^3+6x^2=0$, getting $2x^2(2x+3)=0$; hence $x=0$, $x=-3/2$. At $x=-3/2$ we have $y=-27/8 \cdot 7/2 \approx -11.8$ and $D_x{}^2 y=9>0$; hence we get a minimum. To get all points of inflection, we solve $12x^2+12x=0$, getting $x(x+1)=0$.

At $x=-1$ we have $y=-1$, and we can see, by the above methods, or from what we have of the graph already, that we must have a point of inflection.

Putting this additional information on our drawing, we get the graph shown in Fig. 3-8. Intercepts are at A and B, minimum at C, points of inflection at D and B.

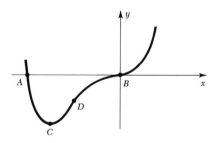

Fig. 3-8

A	$x=-2$
B	$x=0$
C	$x=-3/2$
D	$x=-1$

Further regions of the graph involve nothing of interest.

We do not encourage the reader to proceed by a memorized routine of steps. Use of the general principles above plus common sense should suffice and is a more adaptable approach.

Exercises

1. Sketch the graphs of the following:
   (a) $y=x^3-6x+2$,   (b) $y=\dfrac{2x}{1+x^2}$,
   (c) $y=x^3+3x^2-9x-22$,   (d) $y^3=(x-1)^2\,(x+4)$,
   (e) $y=(x-1)^3$,   (f) $y=x^{4/3}$,
   (g) $y=e^{-x^2}$.

2. Sketch the loci of (x,y) in:
   (a) $y^2=x^3$,   (b) $y^2\,(k-x)=x^3$,
   (c) $x^2y=4\,(2-y)$,   (d) $x=\cot\theta,\ y=\sin^2\theta$.

Problems

3. Sketch the graphs of
   (a) $x^{2/3}+y^{2/3}=a^{2/3}$,
   (b) $x^{1/2}+y^{1/2}=a^{1/2}$ (here $(\ )^{1/2}$ denotes $\pm\surd$),
   (c) $y=\dfrac{e^x+e^{-x}}{2}$ and $y=\dfrac{e^x-e^{-x}}{2}$ on the same set of axes,
   (d) $x=\dfrac{2t^2-2}{1+t^2},\ y=\dfrac{2t^3-2t}{1+t^2}$ (parametric equations for (x,y)).

3.4 Maxima and Minima

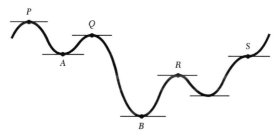

Fig. 3-9

Points such as P, Q, and R, where the graph of $f(x)$ has "peaks" (Fig. 3-9), are said to be points where $f(x)$ attains a *maximum* value. At points such as A and B, $f(x)$ is said to have a *minimum* value.

A maximum value is the greatest value *in its immediate vicinity;* a minimum value is the least. Thus one can have a maximum value that is less than a minimum value—for example, at R and A.

Assuming (as always) that our graph is smooth, the slope at either a maximum or a minimum point must exist and be 0. For a maximum the curve curls downward, hence $D_x^2 y \leqslant 0$. For a minimum, $D_x^2 y \geqslant 0$.

A method of distinguishing the various cases was given in the previous section. Note that at a point such as S one can have $D_x y = 0$ without having either a maximum or a minimum.

To find maximum or minimum values (referred to as *extreme* values) one therefore looks for points where $D_x y = 0$ and then checks the sign of $D_x^2 y$ at each point to see which is which. In many cases it is clear from the nature of the problem that the value is, say, a maximum, or perhaps even the greatest of all values attained by the function, and in such cases one often dispenses with further tests.

(i) As an example, let us find the rectangle of largest area with perimeter 4 (see Fig. 3-10). Let the sides be x and $2-x$. The area is then $A = x\,(2-x) = 2x - x^2$. For maximum A we have $D_x A = 0$; that is, $2 - 2x = 0$, $x = 1$.

Fig. 3-10

We check that the value is actually a maximum by noting that $D_x^2 A = -2 < 0$. Thus, the required rectangle is a square of sides 1.

One can also proceed as follows: Let the sides be x and y (Fig. 3-11a).

$$x + y = 2, \tag{1}$$
$$\text{Area, } A = x \cdot y.$$

Fig. 3-11a

For a maximum, $D_x A = 0$; that is, $x D_x y + y = 0$. From (1), $1 + D_x y = 0$.
Equating values of $D_x y$ gives $-y/x = -1$. Hence $y = x$.

(ii) Maxima and minima are of fundamental importance in physics.
An example in the field of optics is *Fermat's Principle* (Fig. 3-11b).

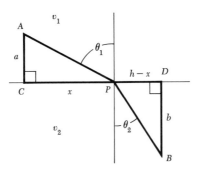

Fig. 3-11b

Consider a beam of light, travelling from a point A in one medium
to a point B in another medium, where the boundary of the two media
is a straight line. Suppose the velocities in the two media are v_1, v_2.
What path should the beam take in order to reach B in the shortest
possible time?

The path obviously must be a straight line within each medium.
It remains to determine the point at which the boundary is to be
crossed. Let a, b, x, C, D, P be as shown in Fig. 3-11, and suppose
$CD = h$. The time taken is a function of x, say $T(x)$, given by

$$T(x) = \frac{AP}{v_1} + \frac{PB}{v_2}$$

$$= \frac{\sqrt{a^2 + x^2}}{v_1} + \frac{\sqrt{(h-x)^2 + b^2}}{v_2}.$$

For a minimum, $D_x T(x) = 0$; that is,

$$\frac{2x}{2\sqrt{a^2 + x^2}} \cdot v_1 - \frac{2(h-x)}{2\sqrt{(h-x)^2 + b^2}} \cdot v_2 = 0.$$

This gives

$$\frac{x}{\sqrt{a^2 + x^2}} \Big/ \frac{h-x}{\sqrt{(h-x)^2 + b^2}} = v_1/v_2;$$

that is,

$$\frac{\sin \theta_1}{\sin \theta_2} = \frac{v_1}{v_2},$$

which is the familiar law of refraction—a law that light is shown experimentally to obey! (To make sure that we have a genuine minimum, the reader is invited to prove that $D_x{}^2T(x)$ is always positive.)

Exercises

1. Find the maximum and minimum values of the functions:
   (a) $3x^2 - x^3$,   (b) $x + 1/x$,
   (c) $1/(1+x^2)$,   (d) $\sin x + \cos x$,
   (e) $3 \sin x + 4 \cos x$,   (f) $2xe^x$,
   (g) $e^{-x} \sin x$,   (h) $6x/(x^2 + 3)$.

2. Find the most economical proportions for a closed circular cylindrical can having a given volume.

3. The force F required to drag a weight W horizontally on a rough surface is

$$\frac{fW}{\cos \theta + f \sin \theta},$$

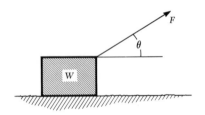

Fig. 3-12

where f is the coefficient of friction and θ is the angle of pull, as shown in Fig. 3-12. Show that for minimum F, $\tan \theta = f$.

4. An object shot vertically upward at a speed u ft. per second reaches a height s ft. in t seconds where $s = ut - 1/2\, gt^2$. Find the maximum height reached.

Problems

5. Find the point on $y^2 = 6x$ nearest the point $(5,0)$. (*Hint:* the distance is to be minimized.)

6. The velocity of a signal in a telegraph cable is $ar^2 \ln (1/r)$ where a is a constant and r is the ratio of the radius of the conducting core to the thickness of the insulation. For what value of r is the velocity greatest?

7. What is the largest circular cylindrical block that can be cut out of a sphere of radius r?

8. Find the dimensions of the largest rectangle that can be inscribed in the ellipse

$$\frac{x^2}{a^2}+\frac{y^2}{b^2}=1.$$

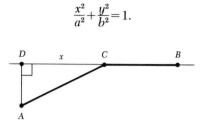

Fig. 3-13

9.
$$AD=1\text{m}.$$
$$DC=x\text{m}.$$
$$DB=4\text{m}.$$

A man can row from A to C at 12 m.p.h., and walk from C to B at 8 m.p.h. Express the total elapsed time as a function of x, and sketch its graph. Try the usual method of finding the path of least time, and discuss the result.

10. Find the smallest value of y on the curve $y^3=x^2$. (Try finding where $D_x y=0$, and comment on the result.)

11. A man wishes to lay a pipe from a point P on the edge of his circular patio to the diametrically opposite point R, proceeding first across under the patio in a straight line to a point Q on the circumference, and thence along the arc by the shortest route to the point concerned. The cost of laying the pipe under the patio is twice as great per foot as the cost of laying it along the circumference.
    (a) What path would *maximize* the cost?
    (b) What path would *minimize* the cost?

12. Two halls, of widths a and b, meet at right angles to form a corner (Fig. 3-14). What is the maximum length of a pole that can be carried horizontally around the corner?

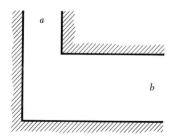

Fig. 3-14

13. A piece of cardboard 10 by 16 inches is to be made into an open box by cutting equal squares out of the corners and turning up the sides. What is the maximum volume obtainable in this way?

14. Find the proportions of a conical tent such that the least amount of canvas is required for a given volume.

15. A right circular cone has radius r and height h. What is the maximum volume of a circular cylinder inscribed in the cone?

16. A rectangle is to be drawn with one side along the x-axis and two corners on the curve $y = e^{-(1/2)x^2}$. What is its maximum area?

17. A package is to be rectangular, with a square cross-section, and the length plus the width can be at most 100 inches. What dimensions give the greatest volume?

3.5 Vector Functions: Differentiation

An important application of differentiation is the determination of the velocity and acceleration of a moving point. Velocity and acceleration are *vectors*, and are best dealt with via the concept of the *derivative of a vector function*. We will assume that the reader has some familiarity with vectors; therefore the basic facts needed will be summarized rather briefly.

There are various aspects of the vector concept. For our purposes, a vector is a directed magnitude and is specified by giving a direction and a number—for example, "5 north," "2 from here toward that steeple," "3 from (1,3) toward (2,7)." For given units of length and time, say feet and seconds, the velocity of a moving point is a vector whose direction is the direction in which the point is moving, and whose number is the number of feet per second at which it is moving. Similarly for acceleration.

We will represent a vector geometrically by an arrow pointing in its direction and whose length, measured in the units we are currently using, is the number of the vector. The notation $\bar{v}$ (or some other barred letter) is used to denote a vector, and the letter without the bar denotes its length. We also denote the vector from the point A to the point B by "$\overline{AB}$." The degenerate case $\overline{AA}$, known as the *zero vector*, and denoted by "$\bar{0}$" is sometimes of use. We note that the direction associated with it is immaterial, since its length is 0. Also, for every vector $\bar{v}$ we have $\bar{0} + \bar{v} = \bar{v}$.

The sum of two vectors $\bar{u}, \bar{v}$ is denoted by "$\bar{u} + \bar{v}$" and is defined as the vector arrived at by laying the $\bar{u}, \bar{v}$ arrows end-to-end as illustrated in Fig. 3-15. (More precisely, the vector represented by the resulting arrow.)

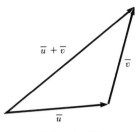

Fig. 3-15

The difference of two vectors $\bar{u}$, $\bar{v}$ is denoted by "$\bar{u} - \bar{v}$" and is defined as shown in Fig. 3-16.

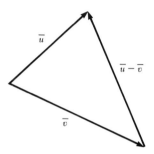

Fig. 3-16

It is a simple exercise to show that $\bar{u} + \bar{v} = \bar{v} + \bar{u}$ and that $\bar{v} + (\bar{u} - \bar{v}) = \bar{u}$ (the latter justifies the use of the term "difference"). It is also easily seen that $\bar{u} + (\bar{v} + \bar{w}) = (\bar{u} + \bar{v}) + \bar{w}$.

For what we will be doing, just one more operation is required—that of multiplying a vector $\bar{v}$ by a number k. The result is denoted by "$k\bar{v}$." If k is *positive*, then $k\bar{v}$ by definition has the same direction as $\bar{v}$ but is k times as long. If k is *negative*, then $k\bar{v}$ has the *opposite* direction to v but is $|k|$ times as long (Fig. 3-17).

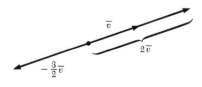

Fig. 3-17

It is a simple exercise to show that

$$\bar{u} - \bar{v} = \bar{u} + (-1)\,\bar{v}.$$

The two following distributive laws are often used.

$$(k+n)\,\bar{u}=k\bar{u}+n\bar{u},$$
$$k(\bar{u}+\bar{v})=k\bar{u}+k\bar{v}.$$

The first follows at once, while the second follows from properties of similar triangles, as we will now show. Take $\overline{OC}=k\bar{u}$ and draw CD parallel to AB, OB meeting CD at D (Fig. 3-18). Then triangles OBA, ODC are similar, $\overline{CD}=k\overline{AB}$, and $\overline{OD}=k\overline{OB}$.

$$k(\bar{u}+\bar{v})=k\overline{OB}$$
$$=\overline{OD}$$
$$=\overline{OC}+\overline{CD}$$
$$=k\bar{u}+k\bar{v}.$$

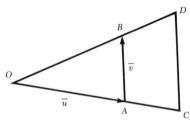

Fig. 3-18

This is a very useful law in applications to geometry, for this distributive property of vector algebra incorporates properties of similar triangles.

A vector-function of a real variable is like a real-valued function of a real variable, except that its values are *vectors* rather than real numbers.

Examples

(i)   Corresponding to every instant of time t seconds after takeoff, an airplane has a velocity vector $\bar{v}(t)$.

(ii)   Corresponding to every mileage reading S miles, a car has a position vector $\bar{u}(S)=\overline{OP}$ relative to a starting point O.

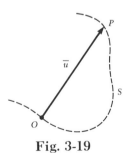

Fig. 3-19

(iii)   If the coordinates of a point P are $x = \cos t$, $y = \sin t$ at time t, then the vector $\overline{OP}$, O being the origin, is a vector-function of t.

The *derivative* of a *vector-function* is defined in a manner exactly analogous to that of a function with numerical values. Thus

$$D_t \bar{v}(t) \text{ means } \lim_{h \to 0} \frac{\bar{v}(t+h) - \bar{v}(t)}{h}.$$

This is the limit of $[1/h \cdot \text{the vector } (\bar{v}\,[t+h] - \bar{v}\,[t])]$. For each value of t this is the limit of a vector-function of h as h approaches 0. Thus the result is a vector-function of t.

To get a clearer picture of what this means geometrically, let us consider Fig. 3-20. Let O be an arbitrarily chosen fixed point. Let P

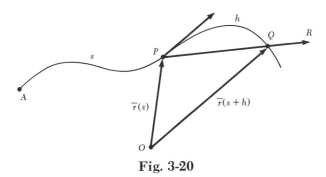

Fig. 3-20

be a point moving along a curve. Let s be the arc length along the curve from a fixed point A on the curve to P. The vector $\overline{OP}$ is then a vector-function of s, say $\overline{OP} = \bar{r}(s)$. We will show that $D_s \bar{r}(s)$ is the *unit tangent vector* (in the direction of s increasing) to the curve at P.

To prove this, note that

$$D_s \bar{r}(s) = \lim_{h \to 0} \frac{\bar{r}(s+h) - \bar{r}(s)}{h}$$

and that $\bar{r}(s+h)$, $\bar{r}(s)$ are the vectors $\overline{OP}$, $\overline{OQ}$ for adjoining points P and Q, h being the arc length from P to Q. Hence $\bar{r}(s+h) - \bar{r}(s)$ is just $\overline{PQ}$, and the quotient whose limit we want is a vector $\overline{PR}$, which is $1/h$ times the vector $\overline{PQ}$. As $h \to 0$, the direction of $\overline{PR}$, being the same as that of $\overline{PQ}$, approaches that of the tangent at P.

The magnitude of $\overline{PR}$ is $1/h$ times the magnitude of $\overline{PQ}$—that is, $1/h$ times the chord length PQ. h being the *arc* length PQ, the magnitude of $\overline{PR}$ is

$$\frac{\text{chord length } PQ}{\text{arc length } PQ}.$$

In Section 3.7 we will argue (intuitively) that the limit of this ratio is always 1 as Q approaches P. Thus the required limit has both the direction and magnitude of the unit tangent vector at P, as required.

We will need two properties of vector differentiation in what follows, namely

$$D_t\left[\bar{u}(t)+\bar{v}(t)\right]=D_t\bar{u}(t)+D_t\bar{v}(t) \tag{1}$$

and

$$D_t\left[a(t)\bar{v}\right]=\left[D_t a(t)\right]\bar{v} \tag{2}$$

where $\bar{v}$ is a fixed vector.

(1)   is easily proven. To prove (2), we have

$$
\begin{aligned}
D_t\left[a(t)\bar{v}\right] &= \lim_{h\to 0}\frac{a(t+h)\bar{v}-a(t)\bar{v}}{h} \\
&= \lim_{h\to 0}\frac{\left[a(t+h)-a(t)\right]\bar{v}}{h} \\
&= \left[\lim_{h\to 0}\frac{a(t+h)-a(t)}{h}\right]\bar{v} \\
&= \left[D_t a(t)\right]\bar{v} \text{ as required.}
\end{aligned}
$$

3.6 Velocity and Acceleration: Components in a Cartesian Coordinate System

If the *position vector* $\overrightarrow{OP}$ of a moving point P is given, relative to a fixed point O, by a vector function of time $\bar{r}(t)$ (Fig. 3-21), then

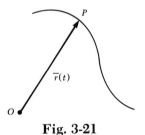

Fig. 3-21

velocity and acceleration are defined as the vectors $D_t\bar{r}(t)$ and $D_t^2\bar{r}(t)$, respectively. We note that the result is independent of the choice of the point O, for suppose we use O' instead (Fig. 3-22), then

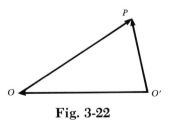

Fig. 3-22

$\overrightarrow{O'P} = \overrightarrow{O'O} + \overrightarrow{OP}$; hence

$$D_t\overrightarrow{O'P} = D_t\overrightarrow{O'O} + D_t\overrightarrow{OP}$$
$$= \overline{0} + D_t\bar{r}(t) \qquad (\overrightarrow{O'O} \text{ being a fixed vector})$$
$$= D_t\bar{r}(t),$$

and hence, also,

$$D_t^2\overrightarrow{O'P} = D_t^2\bar{r}(t).$$

If the equations of motion are given relative to a Cartesian coordinate system, then the Cartesian components of the velocity and acceleration vectors can be found as follows. (We give the result in three dimensions. The analogous results hold in two dimensions.)

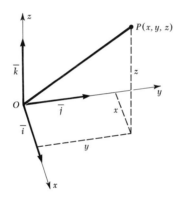

Fig. 3-23

Let $\bar{i}, \bar{j}, \bar{k}$ be the vectors with components $(1,0,0), (0,1,0), (0,0,1)$. Then P has coordinates (x,y,z) if and only if $\overrightarrow{OP} = x\bar{i} + y\bar{j} + z\bar{k}$. OP will serve as the $\bar{r}(t)$ of the above discussion.

Suppose equations of motion $x = a(t)$, $y = b(t)$, $z = c(t)$ are given. Then

$$\bar{r}(t) = a(t)\bar{i} + b(t)\bar{j} + c(t)\bar{k}.$$

Hence

$$D_t\bar{r}(t) = a'(t)\,\bar{i} + b'(t)\,\bar{j} + c'(t)\,\bar{k}$$

and

$$D_t^2\bar{r}(t) = a''(t)\,\bar{i} + b''(t)\,\bar{j} + c''(t)\,\bar{k}.$$

Thus the components of the velocity vector $\bar{v}$ are $[a'(t), b'(t), c'(t)]$ and the components of the acceleration vector $\bar{a}$ are $[a''(t), b''(t), c''(t)]$. (If we had defined $\bar{v}$ and $\bar{a}$ as having these components, we would have had to show that the resulting vectors were independent of the coordinate system used in the definition. The vector differentiation treatment reduces this proof to the almost trivial note above about O' and O).

The magnitudes and directions of $\bar{v}$ and $\bar{a}$ are seen in Fig. 3-24.

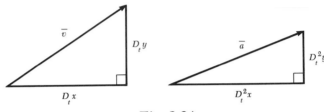

Fig. 3-24

The slope of the velocity vector, it is to be noted, is $D_t y/D_t x$, which is $D_x y$—the slope of the tangent to the curve of motion. Thus the velocity vector always is tangent to the path.

The case of uniform circular motion is of special importance. In Fig. 3-25, let the point $P(x,y)$, move around the circle with radius

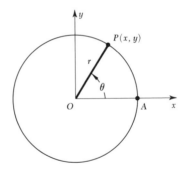

Fig. 3-25

r and centre O in such a way that OP sweeps out K radians per unit time, starting at A at time $t=0$.

Then $\theta = Kt$, and hence $x = r \cos Kt$, $y = r \sin Kt$.

$$D_t x = -Kr \sin Kt, D_t y = Kr \cos Kt$$
$$D_t^2 x = -K^2 r \cos Kt, D_t^2 y = -K^2 r \sin Kt.$$

The velocity has magnitude

$$v = \sqrt{(D_t x)^2 + (D_t y)^2} = Kr$$

and is directed along the tangent.

The acceleration components are $-K^2x, -K^2y$. Its magnitude is

$$\sqrt{K^4x^2 + K^4y^2} = K^2\sqrt{x^2 + y^2} = K^2r,$$

which is conveniently written in terms of v as v^2/r. Since the components of a are $-K^2$ (a negative number) times the components of OP, a must point from P *toward* the origin. Thus, in the case of uniform circular motion, the acceleration is perpendicular to the velocity.

Exercises

1. A point (x,y) moves along a straight line. Prove, from first principles, that the magnitudes of its velocity and acceleration are

$$\sqrt{(D_tx)^2 + (D_ty)^2} \text{ and } \sqrt{(D_t^2x)^2 + (D_t^2y)^2}$$

respectively. (Simple proofs can be given without using vector methods.)

2. Given the following equations of motion, sketch the paths and the velocity and acceleration vectors at the points indicated:
   (a) $x = t-2, y = 3t^3$ when $t = 1$,
   (b) $x = t^4, y = t^3$ when $t = 1$,
   (c) $x = 4\cos 3t, y = 3\sin 3t$ when $t = 0, \pi/9, 2\pi/9, \pi/6$,
   (d) $x = \sin t, y = \sin^2 t$ when $t = \pi/3$ (sketch only the path actually travelled).

Problems

3. A wheel rolls, without slipping and at constant speed, on a straight level road. Prove that the acceleration of a point on the rim of the wheel is constant in magnitude and is always directed toward the center of the wheel.

4. A point moves counterclockwise with a constant speed, 25, around the circle $x^2 + y^2 = 25$. Find the velocity and acceleration vectors at $(3,4)$.

5. A point P moves on the circumference of a circle with radius r. Let w and g be the angular velocity and acceleration, respectively, of the vector joining the center to P. Prove that the magnitudes of the velocity and acceleration vectors are, respectively, rw and

$$r\sqrt{w^4 + g^2}.$$

6. A point moves counterclockwise on the curve $9x^2 + y^2 = 81$ with a speed 5. Find the velocity vector at $(2\sqrt{2}, 3)$.

7. Prove that if the magnitude of the velocity of a moving point is constant, then the velocity and acceleration vectors are always perpendicular to each other.

3.7 The Derivative of Arc Length

In order to find the derivative of one variable with respect to another, one might expect to need to know the functional relation between the two variables in terms of familiar functions. Surprisingly enough (and fortunately), this is not the case.

The length, s, along a given curve, from a fixed point, P, to a point (x,y) is a function of x (Fig. 3-26). We will derive an expression for $D_x s$ in terms of $f(x)$ without knowing any formula connecting s and x.

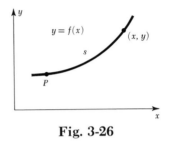

Fig. 3-26

A preliminary theorem is required. It is a theorem of considerable importance and is intuitively quite plausible. Our "proof" will be based on geometrical intuition.

THEOREM: As one point on a curve approaches another, the ratio arc-length/chord-length approaches 1 as limit.

Since we are concerned only with the ratio of lengths, it is not the magnitudes of $\Delta \bar{s}$ (the chord-length) and Δs (the arc-length) which matter, but their relative sizes (see Fig. 3-27), and these clearly

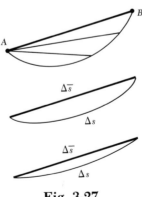

Fig. 3-27

depend on the flatness of the arc from A to B. As B approaches A, the curve changes direction less and less, and hence fits more and more snugly against the line. Hence it is intuitively evident that $\Delta s / \Delta \bar{s}$ approaches 1 as limit. We can now find $D_x s$ as follows:

$$D_x s = \lim_{\Delta x \to 0} \frac{\Delta s}{\Delta x}$$

$$= \lim_{\Delta x \to 0} \frac{\Delta s}{\Delta \bar{s}} \cdot \frac{\Delta \bar{s}}{\Delta x}$$

$$= 1 \cdot \lim_{\Delta x \to 0} \frac{\Delta \bar{s}}{\Delta x} .$$

$\Delta \bar{s}$, however, is just

$$\sqrt{(\Delta x)^2 + (\Delta y)^2} .$$

Hence

$$\frac{\Delta \bar{s}}{\Delta x} = \sqrt{1 + \left(\frac{\Delta y}{\Delta x}\right)^2}$$

and, letting $\Delta x \to 0$, we have

$$D_x s = \sqrt{1 + (D_x y)^2} = \sqrt{1 + [f'(x)]^2} .$$

Thus, we know $D_x s$ [in terms of $f(x)$], without knowing s itself. This at once suggests finding s by *finding a function of x whose derivative with respect to x is the known* $\sqrt{1 + [f'(x)]^2}$—in other words by *anti-differentiation*. We have to stop here, unfortunately, for anti-differentiation in such a case is generally quite difficult. The matter will be dealt with at considerable length in later chapters, where the fundamental importance of anti-differentiation will be explained.

Instead, we pass on to a much simpler application of the result of this section, and then make a few remarks about more general aspects of anti-differentiation.

Problems

1. Let $s(x)$ be the length along the curve $y = 2x^{3/2}/9$ from the origin to the point (x,y).
   (a) Find $D_x s$.
   (b) Find, by inspection, a function of x whose derivative with respect to x is the same as $D_x s$, and whose value at $x = 0$ is 0. (Don't forget D_x constant $= 0$.)

(c) Find the value of this function when $x=4$, and compare with $s(4)$ by drawing a fairly accurate graph and measuring s with a thread.

2. If s denotes arc length measured along a curve from some fixed point on it, prove that the magnitude of the velocity of a point moving on the curve is $D_t s$.

3.8 Curvature

The everyday notion of "curvature" amounts to "rate of turning." The less a curve "curves" or changes direction, the "straighter" it is, and the less is its "curvature." We can get a precise quantitative definition of "curvature" as the rate of change of direction of the curve with respect to some suitably chosen variable. In order to get a result that depends only on the curve itself and not on the choice of axes, we define *curvature* to be *rate of change of direction with respect to distance measured along the curve.* Since we are concerned only with *changes* in direction, the direction of reference is immaterial. We use the positive x-direction for convenience, and use θ as the measure of direction. In Fig. 3-28, we note that $\theta = \tan^{-1}(D_x y)$.

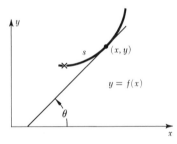

Fig. 3-28

Curvature

$$K = D_s\,\theta = D_x\,\theta \cdot D_s x$$
$$= \frac{D_x{}^2 y}{1 + (D_x y)^2} \cdot \frac{1}{D_x s}$$
$$= \frac{D_x{}^2 y}{1 + (D_x y)^2} \cdot \frac{1}{\sqrt{1 + (D_x y)^2}}$$
$$= \frac{D_x{}^2 y}{[1 + (D_x y)^2]^{3/2}}.$$

Just as the straight line is the curve of constant slope, so the circle is the curve of constant curvature. It is simplest to find the curvature of a circle from first principles (Fig. 3-29).

$$\Delta s = R\,\Delta\theta,$$

Hence

$$K = D_s\,\theta = \lim_{\Delta s \to 0} \frac{\Delta\theta}{\Delta s} = \frac{1}{R}.$$

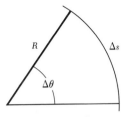

Fig. 3-29

Thus, the curvature of a circle is the reciprocal of its radius.

Just as a curve is often replaced at a given point by its tangent at that point, in circumstances where we are only interested in the first derivative of the variable concerned, so a curve is often replaced by the circle through a point and having the same first and second derivatives as the curve at that point. Since the first two derivatives are the same in both cases, the curvatures must be equal.

The circle in Fig. 3-30 is called the *circle of curvature* at the given point. It is tangent to the curve at the given point (crossing it, however, as a rule), and its radius, called the *radius of curvature* of the curve at the given point, is $1/K$.

Normally we are interested only in the absolute value of the curvature. For this reason, K is often defined as $|D_s\,\theta|$.

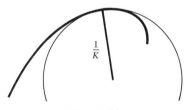

Fig. 3-30

Exercises

1. Draw the circles of curvature to the parabola $y = x^2$ at points where $x = 0, 1, 2, 3$.
2. Find the curvature of a circle from the equation $x^2 + y^2 = R^2$.
3. Find the curvature
   (a) of $x = t - 2$, $y = 3t^2$ at $t = 1$
   (b) of $y^2 - x^2 = 1$ at $(0,1)$
   (c) of $y = x^4$ at $x = 0$.

Problems

4. (a) If $x = f(s)$, $y = g(s)$ are parametric equations of a curve, show that its curvature is

$$K = \frac{x'y'' - y'x''}{(x'^2 + y'^2)^{3/2}}$$

where the primes denote differentiation with respect to s.

   (b) If s is arc length along the curve, prove that

$$K = x'y'' - y'x'' = -x''/y' = y''/x'.$$

5. Express curvature (as defined in Section 3.8) in terms of $D_y x$ and $D_y^2 x$. Having found the result, can you now justify it more simply?

6. Find the point of maximum curvature on the curve $y = e^x$, and locate it on a graph.

7. Find the curvature of the curve $x^2/a^2 + y^2/b^2 = 1$ at $(a,0)$.

8. Two normals are drawn to a curve at A and B. Prove that, as B approaches A, the point of intersection of their normals approaches the center of the circle of curvature as limit. (*Hint:* there is no loss in generality in assuming the curve to be tangent to the x-axis at the origin.)

3.9 Anti-Differentiation

In the study of any process or operation, the question naturally arises as to whether or not it is reversible. In the case of differentiation, we are led to ask the question: "Given $f(x)$, what is *the function of x whose derivative is* $f(x)$?" The full importance of this problem will gradually dawn later. Here our discussion will be brief and introductory.

In the simplest cases, anti-derivatives can be found by inspection. For example, anti-derivatives (with respect to x) of $3x^2$, x^4, $x^{1/2}$, $\cos x$ are x^3, $x^5/5$, $(2/3)x^{3/2}$, $\sin x$.

These are the first to come to mind. We might wonder if any others would do just as well: in other words, are anti-derivatives unique? The answer is certainly no, since $D_x [f(x) + K] = D_x f(x)$ for any constant K. We might wonder if *any* two functions having the same derivative differ only by a constant.

The following fundamental theorems provide an answer.

THEOREM: If $f'(x) \equiv 0$ *then* $f(x)$ *is a constant.*

Proof: $f'(x) \equiv 0$ tells us that the slope of the curve $y = f(x)$ is always zero. Hence this curve must be a straight line parallel to the x-axis, and $f(x)$ is a constant.

THEOREM: If $f'(x) \equiv g'(x)$, then $f(x) \equiv g(x) + C$. (C a constant.)

Proof:

$$D_x[f(x) - g(x)] \equiv f'(x) - g'(x)$$
$$\equiv 0.$$

Hence $f(x) - g(x) \equiv C$ for some constant, C. Thus, the result of anti-differentiation is *unique within an arbitrary added constant.*

We may also ask if $f(x)$ (continous) always has an anti-derivative. The answer is yes—and we have such an anti-derivative in the area under the curve $y = f(x)$, from some arbitrary fixed initial abscissa a to the variable abscissa x (Fig. 3-31). (Our proof rests on the intuitive concept of area and its properties. A more rigorous proof can be given.)

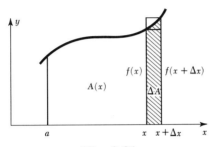

Fig. 3-31

This area, $A(x)$, is clearly a function of x. To find $D_xA(x)$ we notice that, as x changes by Δx, the area increases by an amount ΔA intermediate to the areas of two rectangles, as shown. More precisely

$$f(x) \, \Delta x < \Delta A < f(x + \Delta x) \cdot \Delta x.$$

Hence

$$f(x) < \frac{\Delta A}{\Delta x} < f(x + \Delta x).$$

Now, as $\Delta x \to 0, f(x + \Delta x)$ approaches $f(x)$, and hence $\Delta A/\Delta x$ must too.

Thus

$$D_xA(x) = f(x).$$

(If $f(x)$ is decreasing at the point concerned, the inequalities are reversed, but the result is the same. Also, if $f(x)$ has several ups and downs as x varies from x to $x + \Delta x$, essentially the same argument applies.)

Whether or not we know how to express $A(x)$ in terms of familiar functions of x is another matter. In any case, we can always tabulate its values (approximately) by drawing the graph and counting squares.

A few problems will supplement the remarks of Section 3.7 in indicating the importance of anti-differentiation.

(i)   An object is thrown vertically upward with a velocity v. Express its height as a function of time, taking the acceleration due to gravity to be g.

Let us measure the time, t, from the instant the object is thrown. Then $h=0$ and $D_t h = v$ when $t=0$, h denoting the height. The acceleration is directed downward, hence

$$D_t^2 h = -g.$$

Anti-differentiating this last equation gives $D_t h = -gt + C$. Applying the conditions when $t=0$ gives $v=C$. Hence

$$D_t h = -gt + v.$$

Anti-differentiating again, we get

$$h = -g\frac{t^2}{2} + vt + K.$$

But $h=0$ when $t=0$, hence $K=0$. Therefore,

$$h = -g\frac{t^2}{2} + vt.$$

(ii)   For what curve, or curves, is the slope everywhere twice the x-coordinate of the point concerned?

If $y=f(x)$ is such a curve, then $D_x y = 2x$. Anti-differentiating gives $y=x^2 + C$, for arbitrary C. For each value of C we get a curve satisfying the given condition: these curves form a family of vertical parabolas.

(iii)   The rate of decay of a radioactive substance is a constant, K (positive), times the amount present. Express this amount A as a function of time, assuming that an amount M is present at time $t=0$.

We are given $D_t A = -KA$ (minus because the substance is decaying, not growing).

Collecting the A's gives $1/A\, D_t A = -K$. The left side is recognizable as $D_t \ln A$, and, anti-differentiating, we get $\ln A = -Kt + C$. Hence

$$A = e^{-Kt+C} = e^{-Kt} \cdot e^C.$$

But $A=M$ when $t=0$, hence $M = 1 \cdot e^C$. Therefore,

$$A = e^{-Kt} \cdot M.$$

With this brief introduction to anti-differentiation we conclude our survey of some of the more common applications of the derivative. Much remains, but we shall instead continue with the further development of fundamental notions.

Exercises

1. Find anti-derivatives with respect to x of
   (a) x^3,   (b) $4x^{-2/3}$,
   (c) $2x - 6x^2$,   (d) $2 \sin x$,
   (e) $2 \cos 2x$,   (f) $\sin 7x$,
   (g) $-3e^{-3x}$,   (h) e^{-4x},

   and verify your answers by differentiation.

Problems

2. Find, and describe in geometrical language, the family of all curves along which $D_x^2 y$ is constant. Also find the member of the family which is tangent to the x-axis at the origin and passes through the point $(1,4)$.

3. (a) Find the area bounded by the parabola $y = x^2$, the x-axis and the line $x = 2$. (*Hint:* consider an area $A(x)$ up to the vertical line of intercept x.)
   (b) Find the area under one arch of the curve $y = \sin x$.

Extra Problems

4. Since $\lim_{\Delta x \to 0} \Delta y / \Delta x = D_x y$ we have, for small Δx, $\Delta y / \Delta x \approx D_x y$, hence $\Delta y \approx D_x y \, \Delta x$. Prove that $D_x y \, \Delta x$ is a good approximation to Δy in the sense that the relative error of the approximation approaches 0 as Δx approaches 0.

5. Approximate the value of $\sqrt{8.73}$. ($8.73 = 9 - 0.27$ and $\sqrt{9} = 3$, so take $\Delta x = -0.27$). Check from tables.

6. Approximate the value of $(1.98)^5$. Check by logarithms.

7. Interpret $D_x y \, \Delta x$ in terms of the tangent to $y = f(x)$ at the point at which $D_x y$ is calculated.

8. The radius of a circle increases from 10 inches to 10.1 inches. By approximately how much does the area increase?

9. Without using tables, find approximately $\tan 43°$. ($1° = 0.0175$ radians).

10. The diameter of a circle is measured as 4.2 inches ± 0.05 inch. (a) What is the approximate maximum possible error in the calculated area? (Δ diameter $= 0.05$.) (b) What is approximately the maximum possible *relative* error?

11. A cube is to have a volume of 1000 cu. in. with an allowable error of 2 cu. in. What is approximately the allowable error in the edge?

12. If the edge of a cube can be measured within 0.05 in., approximately how small a cube can be measured if a relative error of 1% can be tolerated in the measurement of its volume?

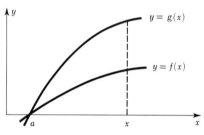

Fig. 3-32

13. $f(x), g(x)$ are two continuous functions such that $f(a)=g(a)=0$, but $g'(a) \neq 0$ (Fig. 3-32). Prove that

$$\lim_{x \to a} \frac{f(x)}{g(x)} = \frac{f'(a)}{g'(a)}$$

(a special case of l'Hôpital's theorem). Note that, since $f(a)=g(a)=0$, we have that $f(x)=\Delta f(x), g(x)=\Delta g(x)$, using $x=a$ as reference point. Also note that as $x \to a$ we have $\Delta x \to 0$. Where does the proof break down if $f(a), g(a)$ are not both 0?

14. Find the following, using the result of problem 12.

(a) $\lim_{x \to 0} \dfrac{1-\cos x}{x}$,

(b) $\lim_{x \to 0} \dfrac{\tan x}{x}$,

(c) $\lim_{x \to a} \dfrac{x-a}{x^n - a^n}$,

(d) $\lim_{x \to 0} \dfrac{p^x - q^x}{x}$,

(e) $\lim_{\theta \to 0} \dfrac{1-\cos \theta}{\sin \theta}$,

(f) $\lim_{x \to 0} \dfrac{\ln (1+x)}{x}$,

(g) $\lim_{x \to \pi/2} \dfrac{\cos x}{x - \pi/2}$

(h) $\lim_{x \to 0} \dfrac{1-\sec x}{x}$.

15. A substance grows at a rate equal to twice the cube root of the amount present (using ounces and seconds as units). The initial amount present is one ounce. How much is present 45/4 seconds later?

16. Given $D_t y = y \cdot t^2$ and that $y=10$ when $t=0$, express y as a function of t.

4

The Definite Integral and the Fundamental Theorem of Calculus

We now turn to the second of the two limiting processes on which calculus is founded, and of which we had a brief view in the first chapter. Here we will see more clearly the exact nature of the problem, and how, in a great many cases, the key to its solution lies in a remarkable connection with the process of differentiation.

4.1 Examples

A few examples will serve to introduce the process we have in mind, and at the same time give an idea of the varied situations in which it may arise.

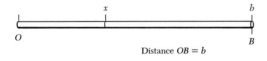

Distance $OB = b$

Fig. 4-1

(i) A straight wire of non-uniform density reaches from O to B (Fig. 4-1). Its density at a distance x from O is a known function of $x, f(x)$. What [in terms of $f(x)$] is the total mass of the wire?

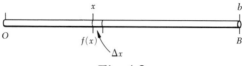

Fig. 4-2

We can form a good approximation to the mass of the wire as follows: Consider the wire as consisting of a very large number of very small pieces, and consider a typical piece, of length Δx (Fig. 4-2). Now $f(x)$ changes very little in value as x varies from one end of the little interval to the other: hence the mass of this little piece will be very nearly $f(x) \cdot \Delta x$ (x being the coordinate of the left end of the piece). The total mass will therefore be approximately the sum of all such approximations for all the little pieces from $x=0$ to $x=b$, denoted

$$\sum_{x=0}^{b} f(x) \cdot \Delta x .$$

If we consider finer and finer subdivisions of the wire, taking all Δx's less than δ (such a δ is known as the *norm* of the subdivision) where δ approaches 0, then not only do the magnitudes of the errors per piece become smaller but, by choosing the correct density at some point in each piece, we take into account, to some extent, the variation in density. Our intuition leads us to expect that the above sum approaches the required mass as limit. Thus

$$\text{mass of wire} = \lim_{\delta \to 0} \sum_{x=0}^{b} f(x) \cdot \Delta x .$$

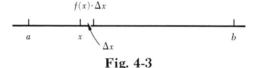

Fig. 4-3

(ii) A particle is moved along the x-axis from $x=a$ to $x=b$ by a force $f(x)$ that is a function of x. What is the total work done by the force?

Again, we divide the interval into small pieces. The work done in pushing the particle along a typical little piece is very nearly $f(x) \cdot \Delta x$, and thus the total work done is approximately

$$\sum_{x=a}^{b} f(x) \cdot \Delta x .$$

As before, we are led to expect that

$$\text{total work done} = \lim_{\delta \to 0} \sum_{x=a}^{b} f(x) \cdot \Delta x.$$

(iii)   Perhaps the most illuminating instance of the limiting process we have in mind is that of the area under a curve. Here we have a clear geometrical interpretation of the error of the approximation, and of the vanishing of this error as the subdivision gets finer and finer.

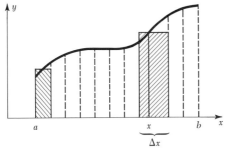

Fig. 4-4

Consider the area lying under the curve $y = f(x)$ from $x = a$ to $x = b$ (Fig. 4-4). A decomposition of the base of this region into little pieces yields a decomposition of the region into vertical strips.

We now generalize slightly the procedure in the previous cases. Let x correspond to an *arbitrary* point somewhere in a typical little interval of length Δx. $f(x)$ is then the height of the curve at this point, and $f(x) \cdot \Delta x$ is the area of the shaded rectangle. This will not (generally) be the area of the strip lying under the curve, but it will be a good approximation to it—the error being at most the sum of two little areas (plus one, and minus the other, to be exact—see Fig. 4-5).

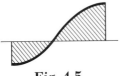

Fig. 4-5

The total area of all such rectangles will therefore be

$$\sum_{x=a}^{b} f(x) \, \Delta x,$$

and this differs from the area under the curve by at most the sum of many little areas of regions lying on the curve (like the teeth of a saw—Fig. 4-6).

Fig. 4-6

It is intuitively evident that, as the norm, δ, of the decomposition approaches 0, the sum of these little areas also approaches 0— *regardless of exactly how the decomposition is performed or of which point we choose within each little interval*—hence the required

$$\text{area} = \lim_{\delta \to 0} \sum_{x=a}^{b} f(x)\, \Delta x.$$

We have assumed here that we understand intuitively what is meant by area. A more satisfactory way of stating our position is that we shall now use the above limit of a sum as a *definition* of area, assuming, on the grounds of intuition concerning area, that it always yields the same result, regardless of our choice of decompositions or choice of points.

(iv)   With slight alterations we can find various properties of the area in (iii), such as its moment of inertia about the y-axis. The moment of inertia of a typical little strip about the y-axis is approximately $x^2 \cdot f(x) \cdot \Delta x$. Summing over all the strips and letting $\delta \to 0$, we are led to

$$I_y = \lim_{\delta \to 0} \sum_{x=a}^{b} x^2 f(x)\, \Delta x,$$

which is our previous process applied to $g(x) = x^2 \cdot f(x)$.

4.2 Evaluating the Limit in a Special Case

The difficulties involved in the evaluation of such limits as we have described become apparent in even the simplest cases. Let us, for example, try to find the area under the curve $y = x^2$ from $x = 0$ to $x = 1$.

We divide the interval from 0 to 1 into n equal parts of length $1/n$, and divide the area into the corresponding strips (Fig. 4-7).

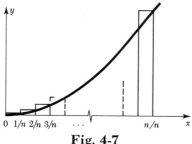

Fig. 4-7

We take as our approximation to the area of each strip $1/n$ times the height at the right end (for convenience) of the strip. These are the areas of the indicated rectangles, namely

$$\frac{1}{n}\left(\frac{1}{n}\right)^2, \frac{1}{n}\left(\frac{2}{n}\right)^2, \cdots, \frac{1}{n}\left(\frac{n}{n}\right)^2.$$

To get $\delta \to 0$ we let $n \to \infty$. Summing and taking the limit, we get

$$\text{Area} = \lim_{n\to\infty} \frac{1}{n^3} [1^2 + 2^2 + \cdots + n^2]$$

$$= \lim_{n\to\infty} \frac{1}{n^3} \frac{n(n+1)(2n+1)}{6}$$

$$= \lim_{n\to\infty} \frac{1(1+1/n)(2+1/n)}{6}$$

$$= \frac{2}{6} = \frac{1}{3}.$$

Although we may be pleased at the result in this particular case, the outlook generally is not very bright. Clearly very substantial difficulties will arise with functions more complicated than the very simple square function.

Before we continue, let us first sum up the preceding with a formal definition and a convenient notation for the limiting process we have in mind.

4.3 The Definite Integral

The following definition is slightly more elaborate than what has gone before: the elaboration consists mainly of stating explicity what we were previously assuming, and the result is applicable under a wider variety of conditions. In most applications, however, we use the simpler forms given above.

Given $f(x)$ (assumed continuous, as usual) and an interval (a,b) for x (including a and b themselves—in Fig. 4-8 $a < b$, but this need

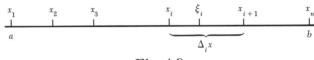

Fig. 4-8

not be the case) let x_1, x_2, ..., x_n, where $x_1 = a$, $x_n = b$, be points of the interval such that each $|\Delta_i x| \leq \delta$, where $\Delta_i x = x_{i+1} - x_i$ (the x's need not all be ordered from a to b: if there is doubling-back, then cancellation takes place). Let ξ_i be an arbitrary value between x_i and x_{i+1}, for every i.

Then

$$\lim_{\delta \to 0} \sum_{i=1}^{n-1} f(\xi_i) \, \Delta_i x \tag{1}$$

is independent of the choice of the x_i's and of the choice of the ξ_i's [*assumed here on intuitive grounds* as in Section 4.1 (iii)] and is denoted by

$$\int_a^b f(x) \, dx. \tag{2}$$

It is called *the definite integral of $f(x)$ from a to b.*

It is to be noted that the *whole* of (2) represents the *whole* of (1). No interpretation is attached to the separate parts of the symbol (2) generally, even though we have preserved the general appearance of (1) for convenience in subsequent operations. The presence of the symbol $\int$ will always indicate that a *limit of a sum* is involved.

4.4 The Law of the Mean

At this point we pause to consider a theorem that we will need in the next section; it is the basis for a number of results of fundamental importance.

The Law of the Mean. If P and Q are two points on a continuous curve $y = F(x)$, for which a derivative exists everywhere between P and Q, then there is some point R on the curve between P and Q where the tangent is parallel to the chord PQ (Fig. 4-9). Thus, for some ξ between p and q,

$$F'(\xi) = \frac{F(q) - F(p)}{q - p}$$

or, as more often used, $F(q) - F(p) = (q - p) F'(\xi)$. This result is geometrically evident (we will not give a rigorous proof here) if we think of moving the chord PQ, *without rotation*, until it just touches the curve at some point R. The former chord will then be the tangent at R, and hence the slope of PQ will be equal to the slope of the tangent at R, as required.

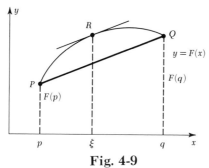

Fig. 4-9

4.5 The Fundamental Theorem of Calculus

The definition of the definite integral of a function is a description of a step-by-step process of finding better and better approximations to its value. This process can always be carried out provided one has at hand a table of values of $f(x)$. It is however, excessively laborious.

In matters of practical convenience and theoretical interest, what we want is a means of expressing the definite integral in terms of familiar functions. This is not generally possible, yet in a great many cases it can not only be done but it can be done very easily. The method, the *Fundamental Theorem of Calculus*, is a connecting link between the two processes of differentiation and integration.

First we will see how the theorem might be guessed at. The ideas involved will then be re-written into a proof.

We are dealing with a sum of terms of the form $f(x)\,\Delta x$. Now the easiest things to add are the differences of a given function of x, for such a sum is just the total change. If only we can find an $F(x)$ such that $\Delta F(x)$ is approximately $f(x)\,\Delta x$, then our sum will be nearly $F(b) - F(a)$.

But $\Delta F(x) \approx f(x)\,\Delta x$ amounts to

$$\frac{\Delta F(x)}{\Delta x} \approx f(x)$$

and taking limits to get rid of our errors, it looks as if what we want is *an $F(x)$ such that $D_x F(x) = f(x)$.*

In Section 3.9 we showed that such an $F(x)$ always exists in the form of an area, $A(x)$, or as we would now say, $\int_a^x f(x)\,dx$.

Thus we suspect the existence of the following:

THEOREM: *If $F'(x) = f(x)$ and $f(x)$ is continuous over the range $a \leqq x \leqq b$, then*

$$\int_a^b f(x)\, dx = F(b) - F(a).$$

For a proof of the theorem, consider the graph of $F(x)$ over the interval (a,b) for x (Fig. 4-10). A decomposition of the interval by

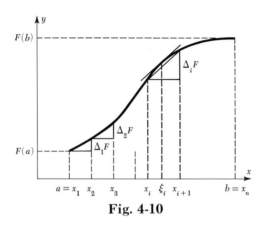

Fig. 4-10

points x_1, x_2, ..., x_n yields, as shown, a sequence of increments $\Delta_1 F$, $\Delta_2 F$, ..., $\Delta_{n-1} F$ in $F(x)$, whose sum is $F(b) - F(a)$. By the Law of the Mean, each $\Delta_i F = F'(\xi_i) \Delta_i x$, for some ξ_i between x_i and x_{i+1}.

Hence

$$F(b) - F(a) = \sum_{i=1}^{n-1} \Delta_i F$$

$$= \sum_{i=1}^{n-1} F'(\xi_i)\, \Delta_i x$$

$$= \sum_{i=1}^{n-1} f(\xi_i)\, \Delta_i x.$$

If we now let the δ of the decomposition approach 0, the right side becomes $\int_a^b f(x)\, dx$ and the left side remains as it is.

Thus we have a connection between the two basic processes of calculus—differentiation and integration. To *integrate* $f(x)$ between the limits a and b, we first find an $F(x)$ *whose derivative is $f(x)$*, and the required integral is then $F(b) - F(a)$. This result (or some essentially equivalent result, depending on how the subject is presented) is the Fundamental Theorem of Calculus. This theorem also has several generalizations that are of fundamental importance in the theory of functions of several variables.

As an illustration, let us evaluate the area in Section 4.2 by use of the Fundamental Theorem. $x^3/3$ is a function whose derivative with respect to x is x^2. The required area is therefore $1^3/3 - 0^3/3 = 1/3$.

Exercises

(In each case in both Exercises and Problems, explain fully the setting-up of the integral in the form $\lim \Sigma \ldots$)

1. Find the areas bounded by:
   (a) The curve $y = x^3$, the y-axis, and the line $y = 2$.
   (b) The curve $y = x^3$, the x-axis, and the lines $x = 1$, $x = 2$.
   (c) The curve $y = x^3$ and the line $7x - y - 6 = 0$.

2. A rectangular plate has sides a and b and unit density. Find its moment and moment of inertia about a line parallel to the side of length b and a distance k from it.

3. Find the moment about the y-axis of the region (assume unit density) bounded by the curve $y = x^4$, the x-axis and the line $x = 1$.

4. The force, in foot-pounds, required to stretch a certain spring x feet is $10x$. Find the work required to stretch it from a 1 foot extension to a 3 foot extension. (Assume force proportional to stretch.)

Problems*

5. Find the moments about the x and y axes of the region bounded by the curve $y = -x^2 + 4x - 3$ and the x-axis.

6. The region bounded by the curve $y = x^3$, the x-axis, and the line $x = 2$ is rotated about the x-axis. Find the volume swept out.

7. Evaluate $\int_{-1}^{+1} x^3 - x \, dx$ and interpret the result in terms of areas.

8. A chain 50 feet long and weighing 2 pounds per foot hangs by its end from a pulley. By pulling horizontally at the top the chain is hauled in. Find the work done.

9. One charged particle is attracted toward another by a force k/x^2, where x is the distance between them. Find the work done in increasing the separation from a to b.

10. Assuming that the derivatives $f'(x)$, $g'(x)$ exist throughout $a \leqslant x \leqslant b$ and that $g'(x) \neq 0$ throughout $a < x < b$, prove that

*The reader will find these problems easier to do after he has studied Chapter 6, but he is urged to do his best with them now.

$$\frac{f(b)-f(a)}{g(b)-g(a)}=\frac{f'(x_1)}{g'(x_1)}$$

for at least one value x_1 between a and b. (Apply the Law of the Mean to the function

$$F(x)=f(x)-f(a)-\frac{f(b)-f(a)}{g(b)-g(a)}[g(x)-g(a)],$$

noting that $F(a)=F(b)=0$.)

11. If $f(a)=g(a)=0$ and $g'(x)\neq0$ throughout $a<x<b$ [assume also, as usual, that $f'(x)$, $g'(x)$ exist], prove that

$$\lim_{x\to a}\frac{f(x)}{g(x)}=\lim_{x\to a}\frac{f'(x)}{g'(x)}.$$

12. Find (if necessary, using the above result several times):

(a) $\lim\limits_{x\to0}\dfrac{\sin x-x}{x^3}$,

(b) $\lim\limits_{x\to0}\dfrac{\ln\sec x}{x^2}$,

(c) $\lim\limits_{y\to1}\dfrac{1+\cos\pi y}{(y-1)^2}$,

(d) $\lim\limits_{x\to0}\dfrac{x^2\cos x}{1-\cos x}$,

(e) $\lim\limits_{\theta\to0}\dfrac{1-\cos^4\theta}{\theta^2}$,

(f) $\lim\limits_{x\to0}\dfrac{\tan x-x}{x^3}$.

5

Anti-Differentiation

We have seen that there are times when we would like to find a function $F(x)$ *whose derivative with respect to* x *is a given* $f(x)$, that is, *an anti-derivative* of $f(x)$.

Finding such anti-derivatives is not nearly so straightforward a process as differentiation; nevertheless there are certain routines that are widely applicable, and we will consider the most common of these.

5.1 Notation, Existence, Uniqueness

To talk about anti-derivatives, it is desirable to have a convenient notation—one well adapted to the applications we most often have in mind. The notation that is almost universally used comes from the fact that $\int_a^x f(x)\,dx$ (a being fixed) is an anti-derivative of $f(x)$ (see Section 3.9). The geometrical interpretation (Fig. 5-1) is the area of the shaded region.

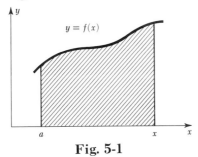

$y = f(x)$

Fig. 5-1

A proof of this can now be given via the Fundamental Theorem, for suppose $F'(x) = f(x)$, then

$$\int_a^x f(x)\,dx = F(x)\Big|_a^x = F(x) - F(a),$$

the derivative of which is $F'(x) = f(x)$.

We assume that the reader accepts, on intuitive grounds, the fact that the above area function, and hence an anti-derivative, exists.

As we have seen (Section 3.9), the result is not unique, but two different anti-derivatives of the same function differ only by an added constant. Hence $\int_a^x f(x)\,dx + C$, C being an arbitrary constant, is the general anti-derivative of $f(x)$ (with respect to x). This is traditionally abbreviated as $\int f(x)\,dx$ and read as "the (indefinite) integral of eff of eks dee eks."

In deriving the results of this chapter, we will use only the fact that the above is an anti-derivative, and will not directly make use of the fact that it can be interpreted as an integral (limit of a sum). It would also be possible, and in some ways preferable, to work directly with the definite integral, but we shall not do so.

Problem

1. Show that it is not always possible to get all anti-derivatives of $f(x)$ by varying a in

$$\int_a^x f(x)\,dx.$$

Thus, to get the general case, an arbitrary constant C must be added.

5.2 An Alternative Notation*

The traditional notation explained above can lead to pitfalls for the unwary student—not so much in technique as in understanding. Another approach, which leads to the same manipulative convenience and at the same time avoids the pitfalls, consists in, first of all, writing $F'(x) = f(x)$ in parametric form,

$$\frac{D_t F(x)}{D_t x} = f(x),$$

from which we get $D_t F(x) = f(x)D_t x$. Using D_t^{-1} as a natural notation for an anti-derivative with respect to t (in differential equations this is usually written as $1/D$) we then get

*This section may be omitted.

$$F(x) = D_t^{-1} f(x) \, D_t x.$$

In applications it is observed that the t subscripts play no role in the manipulations, hence they can conveniently be omitted (we will not go into details here). The final result is the notation $D^{-1} f(x) \, Dx$, exactly paralleling $\int f(x) dx$.

5.3 Basic Formulas

The most obvious anti-differentiation formulas are those got by reading the basic differentiation formulas in reverse, with a few minor alterations for convenience. Thus we get

$$\int f(x) \pm g(x) \, dx = \int f(x) \, dx \pm \int g(x) \, dx$$

$$\int K \cdot f(x) \, dx = K \int f(x) \, dx$$

$$\int x^n \, dx = \frac{x^{n+1}}{n+1} + C \qquad (n \neq -1)$$

$$\int \sin x \, dx = -\cos x + C$$

$$\int \cos x \, dx = \sin x + C$$

$$\int (1 + \tan^2 x) \, dx = \tan x + C$$

$$\int \frac{1}{\sqrt{1-x^2}} \, dx = \sin^{-1} x + C$$

$$\int \frac{-1}{\sqrt{1-x^2}} \, dx = \cos^{-1} x + C$$

$$\int \frac{1}{1+x^2} \, dx = \tan^{-1} x + C$$

$$\int e^x \, dx = e^x + C$$

$$\int \frac{1}{x} \, dx = \ln x + C \qquad (x > 0).$$

The last formula needs to be adjusted if x ranges over negative values; we then have

$$D_x \ln(-x) = D_{-x} \ln(-x) \cdot D_x(-x)$$

$$= \frac{1}{-x} \cdot (-1)$$

$$= \frac{1}{x}.$$

Thus, for negative x,

$$\int \frac{1}{x} dx = \ln(-x) + C.$$

Both results can be combined in the one formula

$$\int \frac{1}{x} dx = \ln |x| + C.$$

The quotient rule of differentiation does not yield a useful anti-differentiation formula. The product rule does, but we will postpone its use for a few pages.

The chain rule of differentiation yields what might be called a *chain rule of anti-differentiation,* namely

$$\int f(x) \, dx = \int f(x) \, D_t x \, dt,$$

where x is assumed to be some function of t. This says that a function whose derivative with respect to x is $f(x)$ is a function whose derivative with respect to t is $f(x) D_t x$. This follows at once from the chain rule of differentiation, for if $D_x F(x) = f(x)$, then $D_t F(x) = f(x) D_t x$.

Note that the chain rule of anti-differentiation amounts to the interchangeability of the expressions dx and $D_t x \, dt$ as parts of the total expression for the anti-derivative. No meaning is given for these expressions in isolation; but we will allow ourselves to write $dx = D_t x \, dt$ as a shorthand for this condition of interchangeability.

One further basic result is that, as with differentiation, *the name of the variable does not matter.* For example

$$\int \cos t \, dt = \sin t + C,$$

$$\int \cos z \, dz = \sin z + C,$$

$$\int \cos \sqrt{x} \, d\sqrt{x} = \sin \sqrt{x} + C,$$

$$\int \cos \sqrt{x^2 + x} \, d\sqrt{x^2 + x} = \sin \sqrt{x^2 + x} + C.$$

Exercises

1. Complete the list of basic differentiation formulas as follows:
   $dx^n = nx^{n-1} dx$, etc.

2. Express in terms of d of the variable involved:

   (a) $d \sin \sqrt{t}$,

   (b) $d \dfrac{1 + \ln z}{z}$,

   (c) $d \, 1/(1 + e^x)$,

   (d) $d \, e^t \sin t$,

(e) $d \dfrac{\sin u}{\ln u}$,   (f) $d (1 + e^{\sqrt{x}})^6$,

(g) $d \cos 1/x$,   (h) $d\, t^2(1 + \tan^{-1}t)$,

(i) $d (\theta + \sin \theta \cos \theta)$.

3. Find a function:
   (a) whose derivative with respect to x^2 is x^6,
   (b) whose derivative with respect to x^2 is $\sin x/x$,
   (c) whose derivative with respect to $\sqrt{x}$ is $x^{3/2}$,
   (d) whose derivative with respect to t is $2x \cos x^2\, D_t x$.

5.4 "Elementary" Anti-Differentiations

The following examples illustrate the direct application of the above rules.

1. $\int x^4\, dx = \dfrac{x^5}{5} + C$.

2. $\int x^3 + \dfrac{1}{x^2}\, dx = \int x^3\, dx + \int \dfrac{1}{x^2}\, dx$

$$= \frac{x^4}{4} + \int x^{-2}\, dx$$

$$= \frac{x^4}{4} + \frac{x^{-2+1}}{-2+1} + C$$

$$= \frac{x^4}{4} - \frac{1}{x} + C.$$

3. $\int \sin \theta - \cos \theta\, d\theta = \int \sin \theta\, d\theta - \int \cos \theta\, d\theta$

$$= -\cos \theta - \sin \theta + C.$$

4. $\int \dfrac{1}{1+z^2}\, dz = \tan^{-1} z + C$.

5. $\int 4e^t + 6 \sin t - 7t^9\, dt$

$$= \int 4e^t\, dt + \int 6 \sin t\, dt - \int 7t^9\, dt$$

$$= 4 \int e^t\, dt + 6 \int \sin t\, dt - 7 \int t^9\, dt$$

$$= 4 e^t - 6 \cos t - 7 \frac{t^{10}}{10} + C.$$

6. $\int \cos x \sin x\, dx = -\int \cos x\, d \cos x$

$$= -\frac{\cos^2 x}{2} + C.$$

7. $\int (x^2+2x)(2x+2)\,dx = \int (x^2+2x)\,d\,(x^2+2x)$

$$= \frac{(x^2+2x)^2}{2} + C.$$

8. $\int e^{2t}\,2\,dt = \int 2t\,e^{2t}\,d\,2t$

$$= e^{2t} + C.$$

9. $\int \sin^3 t \cos\,dt = \int \sin^3 t\,d\sin t$

$$= \frac{\sin^4 t}{4} + C.$$

10. $\int \tan^2 t\,(1+\tan^2 t)\,dt = \int \tan^2 t\,d\tan t$

$$= \frac{\tan^3 t}{3} + C.$$

11. $\int e^{2kx}\,dx = \int \frac{e^{2kx}}{2k}\,d\,2kx$

$$= \frac{1}{2k} \int e^{2kx}\,d\,2kx$$

$$= \frac{1}{2k} e^{2kx} + C.$$

12. $\int (1+\theta)^{1/2}\,d\theta = \int (1+\theta)^{1/2}\,d\,(1+\theta)$

$$= \frac{(1+\theta)^{3/2}}{3/2} + C.$$

13. $\int \frac{\ln x}{x}\,dx = \int \ln x\,d\ln x$ (x is clearly assumed >0.)

$$= \frac{(\ln x)^2}{2} + C.$$

14. $\int (x^2+2x+2)(2x+2)\,dx = \int (x^2+2x+2)^{1/2}\,d\,(x^2+2x+2)$

$$= \frac{(x^2+2x+2)^{3/2}}{3/2} + C.$$

Exercises

1. Find anti-derivatives with respect to the variables involved:
   (a) $x^2 - 1/x^2$,
   (b) $(2x+1)^2$,
   (c) $1/(x+1)$,
   (d) $1/\sqrt{2t+1}$,
   (e) z/z^2+2,
   (f) $(3u+4)^{19}$,

(g) $7y^3/(2-7y^4)$, (h) $\sin^2 x \cos x$,

(i) $\dfrac{\sin 3\theta}{\cos 3\theta - 3}$, (j) $\dfrac{\sec^2 t}{1+\tan t}$,

(k) $e^z \sqrt{1-e^z}$, (l) $\cos t/\sqrt{1+\sin t}$,

(m) $\tan x$, (n) $x/\sqrt{1-x^4}$,

(o) $ze^{(z^2)}$, (p) $\dfrac{1}{t}(\ln t)^2$,

(q) $(2x+4)\sin(x^2+4x+7)$, (r) $e^x \sin e^x$,

(s) $\sin 5x$, (t) $z \sin(z^2+2)$,

(u) $\dfrac{1+x}{x^2+1}$.

Problems

2. Anti-differentiate with respect to x:
   (a) $1/(5+3x^2)$, (b) $2/(2x^2+4)$,

   (c) $1/\sqrt{(4-x^2)}$, (d) $3/\sqrt{(9-16x^2)}$,

   (e) $1/\sqrt{(a^2+b^2 x^2)}$.

5.5 Anti-Differentiation "by Parts"

The rule

$$D_x f \cdot g = fD_x g + gD_x f \qquad \text{(See 2.4.)}$$

for differentiating a product yields

$$f \cdot g = \int (fD_x g + gD_x f)\, dx = \int fD_x g\, dx + \int gD_x f\, dx$$
$$= \int f\, dg + \int g\, df$$

by the chain rule. When re-arranged into the form

$$\int f\, dg = f \cdot g - \int g\, df$$

this becomes a useful formula in certain cases—for example, when $\int g\, df$ is easier to evaluate then $\int f\, dg$.

The formula is not usually immediately applicable: we first have to put our anti-derivative into the form $\int f(x)\, dg(x)$ in some suitable way.

Examples

1. $\int x\, e^x\, dx = \int x\, de^x$ (the formula now applies)

   $= x \cdot e^x - \int e^x\, dx$

   $= x \cdot e^x - e^x + C$.

2. $\int x \cdot \ln x \, dx = \int \ln x \, d\frac{x^2}{2}$ (the formula now applies)

$$= \ln x \cdot \frac{x^2}{2} - \int \frac{x^2}{2} d \ln x$$

$$= \ln x \cdot \frac{x^2}{2} - \int \frac{x^2}{2} \cdot \frac{1}{x} dx$$

$$= \ln x \cdot \frac{x^2}{2} - \int \frac{x}{2} dx$$

$$= \ln x \cdot \frac{x^2}{2} - \frac{x^2}{4} + C.$$

3. $\int \tan^{-1} x \, dx = \tan^{-1} x \cdot x - \int x \, d\tan^{-1} x$ (applying the formula directly)

$$= \tan^{-1} x \cdot x - \int \frac{x}{1+x^2} dx$$

$$= \tan^{-1} x \cdot x - 1/2 \int \frac{1}{1+x^2} d(1+x^2)$$

$$= \tan^{-1} x \cdot x - 1/2 \ln (1+x^2) + C.$$

It is already becoming apparent that a certain amount of ingenuity is needed for the effective use of our formulas. This is characteristic of anti-differentiation. Sometimes the "by parts" process must be carried out several times before a solution is obtained.

4. $\int e^x \sin x \, dx = \int \sin x \, de^x$

$$= \sin x \cdot e^x - \int e^x \, d\sin x \quad \text{(applying formula)}$$

$$= \sin x \cdot e^x - \int e^x \cos x \, dx$$

$$= \sin x \cdot e^x - \int \cos x \, de^x$$

$$= \sin x \cdot e^x - \cos x \, e^x + \int e^x \, d\cos x \quad \text{(applying formula)}$$

$$= \sin x \cdot e^x - \cos x \, e^x - \int e^x \sin x \, dx.$$

This equation can now be solved for $\int e^x \sin x \, dx$, giving

$$\int e^x \sin x \, dx = \frac{e^x (\sin x - \cos x)}{2} + C \quad \text{(putting in a constant)}.$$

Problems

1. Anti-differentiate with respect to x
   (a) $x \cos 2x$,   (b) $\sin^{-1} x$,
   (c) $x^2 \cos 3x$,   (d) $x \sin x$,

(e) $x^3 \ln x$,   (f) $\ln x$,

(g) $(\ln x)^2$,   (h) $x^3 e^x$,

(i) $x^3 e^{-x^2}$,   (j) $x^3 \sqrt{(x^2+1)}$,

(k) $x^3/(1+x^2)^2$,   (l) $e^{-x} \cos x$.

5.6 Rational Functions

In this section it will be shown how anti-derivatives of the type

$$\int \frac{P(x)}{Q(x)}\, dx \quad (P, Q \text{ polynomials})$$

can always be evaluated in terms of the "elementary" functions with which we have been dealing. The procedure can always be carried out in principle, and it can be carried out in practice whenever we know the real linear and quadratic factors of $Q(x)$.

If the degree of P is not less than that of Q, our first step is to divide $Q(x)$ into $P(x)$, getting

$$\frac{P(x)}{Q(x)} = R(x) + \frac{S(x)}{Q(x)},$$

where R and S are polynomials and the degree of S is less than that of Q. $R(x)$ is easily anti-differentiated, and we are left with a case where *degree of numerator* is less than *degree of denominator*. So it remains only to consider cases where the degree of P is less than the degree of Q.

The Fundamental Theorem of Algebra and the theorem that complex roots of a polynomial always occur in conjugate pairs guarantee between them that $Q(x)$ can be completely factored into real linear and quadratic factors. (*Exercise:* prove this.) Moreover, every real quadratic either is of the form

$$a\,[(x-p)^2+q^2]$$

or can be split into real linear factors. (*Exercise:* prove this.) Gathering together all equal factors, we get

$$Q(x) = C(a_1 x + b_1)^{n_1} \cdots (a_k x + b_k)^{n_k} \,[(x-p_1)^2 + q_1{}^2]^{m_1}$$
$$\cdots [(x-p_h)^2 + q_h{}^2]^{m_h}$$

where the n's and m's are the number of times each factor occurs.

Suppose now that we have found such a factorization of $Q(x)$ (we know it exists, but finding it may be another matter). The algebraic theory of partial fractions guarantees that $P(x)/Q(x)$ can be expressed as a sum of terms of the following forms:

(a) For *each* factor $(a_i x + b_i)^{n_i}$ of $Q(x)$:

$$\frac{A_1}{a_i x + b_i} + \frac{A_2}{(a_i x + b_i)^2} + \cdots + \frac{A_{n_i}}{(a_i x + b_i)^{n_i}}.$$

(b) For *each* factor $[(x-p_j)^2+q_j^2]^{m_j}$ of $Q(x)$:

$$\frac{B_1x+C_1}{(x-p_j)^2+q_j^2}+\frac{B_2x+C_2}{[(x-p_j)^2+q_j^2]^2}+\cdots+\frac{B_{m_j}x+C_{m_j}}{[(x-p_j)^2+q_j^2]^{m_j}},$$

the A's, B's and C's being constants.

To find such a splitting into "partial fractions" we equate $P(x)/Q(x)$ to such a sum and, by equating coefficients and solving the resulting equations, or by other methods (to be described), find the A's, B's, and C's. (One can always verify that the result is correct by direct calculation.)

Examples

(i)
$$\frac{3x}{x^2-x-2}.$$

The denominator factors easily, giving

$$\frac{3x}{(x+1)(x-2)}.$$

Suppose

$$\frac{3x}{(x+1)(x-2)}=\frac{A}{x+1}+\frac{B}{x-2}\qquad \text{(identically)}.$$

(Here we have only two linear terms, with $n=1$ in each.) The right side is

$$\frac{Ax-2A+Bx+B}{(x+1)(x-2)}=\frac{x(A+B)-2A+B}{(x+1)(x-2)}. \tag{1}$$

Equating coefficients gives $A+B=3$ and $-2A+B=0$, since $3x+0 \equiv (A+B)x+(-2A+B)$, whence $A=1$, $B=2$. Thus

$$\frac{3x}{(x+1)(x-2)}=\frac{1}{x+1}+\frac{2}{x-2}. \tag{2}$$

One could proceed otherwise at step (1), noting that $3x=A(x-2)+B(x+1)$ must hold for all x. Putting $x=2$ gives $6=B\cdot3$, hence $B=2$. Putting $x=-1$ gives $-3=A(-3)$, hence $A=1$. One can usually pick out some constants very quickly by this method.

(ii)
$$\frac{x^3+1}{x(x^2+1)^2}\text{ is supposed equal to }\frac{A}{x}+\frac{Bx+C}{(x^2+1)}+\frac{Dx+E}{(x^2+1)^2}.$$

The right side is

$$\frac{A(x^2+1)^2+(Bx+C)x(x^2+1)+(Dx+E)x}{x(x^2+1)^2}.$$

Expanding, equating coefficients, and solving gives $A=1$, $B=-1$, $C=1$, $D=-1$, $E=-1$, hence

$$\frac{x^3+1}{x(x^2+1)^2}=\frac{1}{x}-\frac{x-1}{x^2+1}-\frac{x+1}{(x^2+1)^2}.$$

The next, and final, step is to anti-differentiate the separate terms. These are of two kinds. First,

$$\frac{A}{(ax+b)^n},$$

and second,

$$\frac{Bx+C}{[(x-p)^2+q^2]^m}.$$

Under the first we have two possibilities. If $n=1$, then we have

$$\int \frac{A}{ax+b}\,dx=\frac{1}{a}\int \frac{A}{ax+b}\,d(ax+b)$$

$$=\frac{A}{a}\ln|ax+b|.$$

If $n\neq 1$, then we have

$$\int \frac{A}{(ax+b)}n\,dx=\frac{A}{a}\int \frac{1}{(ax+b)^n}\,d(ax+b)$$

$$=\frac{A}{a}\cdot\frac{(ax+b)^{-n+1}}{-n+1}.$$

The second kind, apart from a constant factor, is of the form

$$\frac{x+c}{[(x-p)^2+q^2]^m}.$$

If $m=1$, then we have

$$\int \frac{x+c}{(x-p)^2+q^2}\,dx=\int \frac{x-p+p+c}{(x-p)^2+q^2}\,dx$$

$$=\int \frac{x-p}{(x-p)^2+q^2}\,dx+\int \frac{p+c}{(x-p)^2+q^2}\,dx$$

$$=1/2\int \frac{1}{(x-p)^2+q^2}\,d\,[(x-p)^2+q^2]+\frac{1}{q^2}\int \frac{p+c}{\left(\frac{x-p}{q}\right)^2+1}\,dx$$

$$=1/2\ln\,[(x-p)^2+q^2]+\frac{(p+c)q}{q^2}\tan^{-1}\frac{x-p}{q}.$$

In the case where $m \neq 1$, we will give a "reduction formula" that will provide a step-by-step procedure to reduce the problem eventually to a case where m is 1.

The first two steps are as above, but now the term

$$\int \frac{p+c}{[(x-p)^2+q^2]^m}\,dx$$

requires special treatment (the other is easily handled). Removing the constant factor $p+c$ and setting $x-p=z$ for convenience gives

$$\int \frac{1}{[z^2+q^2]^m}\,dz,$$

since $dx=d(x-p)=dz$. This further simplifies to

$$\frac{1\cdot q}{q^{2m}}\int \frac{1}{[(z/q)^2+1]^m}\,D\,z/q.$$

By setting $z/q=t$, this is, apart from a constant factor,

$$\int \frac{1}{(t^2+1)^m}\,dt.$$

The final stages are now

$$\int \frac{1}{(t^2+1)^m}\,dt = \int \frac{1+t^2-t^2}{(t^2+1)^m}\,dt$$

$$= \int \frac{1+t^2}{(t^2+1)^m}\,dt - \int \frac{t^2}{(t^2+1)^m}\,dt$$

$$= \int \frac{1}{(t^2+1)^{m-1}}\,dt - 1/2\int \frac{t}{(t^2+1)^m}\,d(t^2+1)$$

$$= K\ (\text{for short}) - 1/2\int t\,d\frac{(t^2+1)^{-m+1}}{-m+1}$$

$$= K + \frac{1}{2(m-1)}\int t\,d\,(t^2+1)^{-m+1}$$

$$= K + \frac{t(t^2+1)^{1-m}}{2(m-1)} - \frac{1}{2(m-1)}\int (t^2+1)^{1-m}\,dt \quad (\text{by parts})$$

$$= K + \frac{t(t^2+1)^{1-m}}{2(m-1)} - \frac{1}{2(m-1)}\cdot K.$$

We have succeeded in expressing

$$\int \frac{1}{(t^2+1)^m}\,dt$$

in terms of K, which is

$$\int \frac{1}{(t^2+1)^{m-1}}\,dt.$$

By repeating this process (done by repeated use of the formula now established) the power of (t^2+1) can be eventually whittled down to 1, and the original anti-derivative evaluated.

Thus, once all the real linear and quadratic factors of $Q(x)$ have been found, the anti-differentiation of $P(x)/Q(x)$ can be carried out by routine methods in terms of the elementary functions.

We illustrate this by anti-differentiating examples (i) and (ii), whose partial fraction forms have already been found.

(i)

$$\int \frac{3x}{x^2-x-2}\,dx = \int \frac{1}{x+1}+\frac{2}{x-2}\,dx$$

$$= \int \frac{1}{x+1}\,dx + 2\int \frac{1}{x-2}\,dx$$

$$= \ln|x+1|+2\ln|x-2|+C.$$

(ii)

$$\int \frac{x^3+1}{x\,(x^2+1)^2}\,dx = \int \frac{1}{x}-\frac{x+1}{x^2+1}-\frac{x+1}{(x^2+1)^2}\,dx.$$

Working each part separately, we get

$$\int \frac{1}{x}\,dx = \ln|x|,$$

$$-\int \frac{x+1}{x^2+1}\,dx = -\int \frac{x}{x^2+1}\,dx - \int \frac{1}{x^2+1}\,dx$$

$$= -\frac{1}{2}\int \frac{1}{x^2+1}\,d\,(x^2+1) - \tan^{-1}x$$

$$= -\frac{1}{2}\ln\,(x^2+1) - \tan^{-1}x,$$

$$-\int \frac{x+1}{(x^2+1)^2}\,dx = -\int \frac{x}{(x^2+1)^2}\,dx - \int \frac{1}{(x^2+1)^2}\,dx$$

$$= -\frac{1}{2}\int \frac{1}{(x^2+1)^2}\,d\,(x^2+1) - \int \frac{1+x^2-x^2}{(x^2+1)^2}$$

$$= \frac{1}{2}\,(x^2+1)^{-1} - \int \frac{1+x^2}{(x^2+1)^2}\,dx + \int \frac{x^2}{(x^2+1)^2}\,dx$$

$$= \frac{1}{2\,(x^2+1)} - \int \frac{1}{x^2+1}\, dx + \frac{1}{2} \int \frac{x}{(x^2+1)^2}\, d\,(x^2+1)$$

$$= \frac{1}{2\,(x^2+1)} - \tan^{-1} x - \frac{1}{2} \int x\, d\,\frac{1}{x^2+1}$$

$$= \frac{1}{2\,(x^2+1)} - \tan^{-1} x - \frac{1}{2}\frac{x}{x^2+1} + \frac{1}{2} \int \frac{1}{x^2+1}\, dx$$

$$= \frac{1}{2\,(x^2+1)} - \tan^{-1} x - \frac{1}{2}\frac{x}{x^2+1} + \frac{1}{2} \tan^{-1} x$$

$$= \frac{1}{2\,(x^2+1)} - \frac{1}{2}\frac{x}{x^2+1} - \frac{1}{2} \tan^{-1} x.$$

Putting the parts together, we get

$$\int \frac{x^3+1}{x\,(x^2+1)^2}\, dx = \ln(x) - \frac{1}{2} \ln(x^2+1) - \frac{3}{2} \tan^{-1} x + C.$$

As an additional example, consider the following:

(iii)

$$\int \frac{x+5}{x^3+4x^2+7x+6}\, dx.$$

By inspection we see that $x=-2$ is a root of the denominator, hence $x+2$ is a factor. By division we find that the other factor is x^2+2x+3. By the discriminant test, x^2+2x+3 has no real linear factors. By "completing the square" we see that it can be written as $(x+1)^2+2$. Hence we look for partial fractions as follows:

$$\frac{x+5}{(x+2)[(x+1)^2+2]} = \frac{A}{x+2} + \frac{Bx+C}{(x+1)^2+2}$$

$$= \frac{A\,(x^2+2x+3) + (Bx+C)\,(x+2)}{(x+2)[(x+1)^2+2]}$$

$$= \frac{(A+B)\,x^2 + (2A+2B+C)\,x + 3A+2C}{(x+2)[(x+1)^2+2]}.$$

Equating coefficients in the numerator, we get

$$A+B=0,$$

$$2A+2B+C=1,$$

$$3A+2C=5,$$

from which it follows that $A=1$, $B=-1$, $C=1$.

Thus

$$\int \frac{x+5}{(x+2)[(x+1)^2+2]}\, dx = \int \frac{1}{x+2}\, dx + \int \frac{-x+1}{(x+1)^2+2}\, dx$$

$$= \ln|x+2| - \int \frac{x+1-2}{(x+1)^2+2}\, dx$$

$$= \ln|x+2| - \int \frac{x+1}{(x+1)^2+2}\, d\,(x+1) + \int \frac{2}{(x+1)^2+2}\, dx$$

$$= \ln|x+2| - \frac{1}{2}\int \frac{1}{(x+1)^2+2}\, d[\,(x+1)^2+2] + \sqrt{2}\int \frac{1}{\frac{(x+1)^2}{2}+1}\, d\frac{x+1}{\sqrt{2}}$$

$$= \ln|x+2| - \frac{1}{2}\ln\,[(x+1)^2+2] + \sqrt{2}\tan^{-1}\frac{x+1}{\sqrt{2}} + C\,.$$

Problems

1. Anti-differentiate with respect to x

(a) $\dfrac{4x+2}{2x-1}$,

(b) $\dfrac{4x^2+x+1}{x^3-1}$,

(c) $\dfrac{1}{x^2\,(x^2-4)}$,

(d) $\dfrac{1}{(x-2)\,(x-4)}$,

(e) $\dfrac{1}{x^2+2x+5}$,

(f) $\dfrac{x^2+6x-1}{(x-3)^2(x-1)}$,

(g) $\dfrac{1}{x^2-1}$,

(h) $\dfrac{5x+3}{x^2-6x-7}$,

(i) $\dfrac{x-1}{(x-2)^2}$,

(j) $\dfrac{x^2}{(1-x^2)^2}$,

(k) $\dfrac{e^x}{1-e^{2x}}$,

(l) $\dfrac{1}{e^x-1}$,

(m) $\dfrac{4x^2+6}{x^3+3x}$,

(n) $\dfrac{4x^2+2x+8}{x\,(x^2+2)^2}$.

5.7 Change of Variable (Substitution)

In carrying out such an anti-differentiation as

$$\int x \sin x^2\, dx = 1/2 \int \sin x^2\, dx^2$$

$$= -1/2 \cos x^2 + C$$

we have, in effect, used x^2 as a new variable. This could have been done by a formal substitution as follows.

Set $x^2 = t$. Then $dx^2 = 2x\,dx = dt$ (see Section 5.3 concerning $dx = D_t x\,dt$). Therefore

$$\int x \sin x^2\,dx = \int \sin t \cdot 1/2\,dt$$

$$= -1/2 \cos t + C$$

$$= -1/2 \cos x^2 + C \qquad \text{(returning to } x\text{)}.$$

The advantage of a formal substitution is that, once it has been made, the subsequent steps become more mechanical and the expressions involved take on a simpler form. With relatively easy anti-differentiations, however, it is just as simple to proceed as we have been doing.

As an illustration of the power of the method of substitution, we shall see how, by a change of variable, a very large and important class of anti-differentiations can be reduced to the anti-differentiation of rational functions.

5.8 Rational Functions of Trigonometric Functions

Anti-derivatives such as

$$\int \sin^5 x\,dx, \qquad \int \sin^2 x \cdot \cos^2 x\,dx,$$

$$\int \frac{1}{\cos x}\,dx, \qquad \int \frac{2 \sin^2 x}{\cos x + \cos^2 x}\,dx$$

are all special cases of the type $\int R (\sin x, \cos x)\,dx$, where R is a rational function of two variables.

It is a well-known result in trigonometry that $\sin x$ and $\cos x$ (and hence all the trigonometric functions) are rational functions of $\tan x/2$.

This suggests making the substitution $\tan x/2 = t$, that is, making $\tan x/2$ our new variable and calling it t (Fig. 5-2). We then have

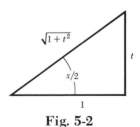

Fig. 5-2

$$\sin x = 2 \sin \frac{x}{2} \cos \frac{x}{2}$$

$$= \frac{2t}{\sqrt{1+t^2}} \cdot \frac{1}{\sqrt{1+t^2}}$$

$$= \frac{2t}{1+t^2},$$

$$\cos x = 2 \cos^2 \frac{x}{2} - 1$$

$$= 2 \left(\frac{1}{\sqrt{1+t^2}} \right)^2 - 1$$

$$= \frac{1-t^2}{1+t^2}.$$

Furthermore, $x = 2 \tan^{-1} t$, hence

$$dx = \frac{2}{1+t^2} dt.$$

The anti-derivative thus becomes

$$\int R \left(\frac{2t}{1+t^2}, \frac{1-t^2}{1+t^2} \right) \cdot \frac{2}{1+t^2} dt,$$

which is $\int$ (a rational function of t) dt and can be evaluated by previous methods. Example:

$$\int \frac{1}{\sin x} dx = \int \frac{1+t^2}{2t} \cdot \frac{2}{1+t^2} dt$$

$$= \int \frac{1}{t} dt$$

$$= \ln|t| + C$$

$$= \ln \left| \tan \frac{x}{2} \right| + C.$$

5.9 Powers of Trigonometric Functions

Anti-derivatives such as $\int \sin x^2 \, dx$, $\int \sin^3 x \cos^3 x \, dx$ occur frequently in practice. Although these can be handled as in the previous section, other methods are more convenient. One method involves the use of the identities

(a)

$$\sin 2A = 2 \sin A \cos A \, ,$$

(b)

$$\cos 2A = 2 \cos^2 A - 1$$
$$= 1 - 2 \sin^2 A \, ,$$

which enable us to reduce powers by doubling angles. The following examples illustrate the methods most frequently used.

(i)

$$\int \sin^2 x \cos^3 x \, dx = \int \sin^2 x \cdot \cos^2 x \, d \sin x$$
$$= \int \sin^2 x \, (1 - \sin^2 x) \, d \sin x$$
$$= \int \sin^2 x \, d \sin x - \int \sin^4 x \, d \sin x$$
$$= \frac{\sin^3 x}{3} - \frac{\sin^5 x}{5} + C \, .$$

(This method applies whenever either $\sin x$ or $\cos x$ appears to an odd power.)

(ii)

$$\int \sin^2 x \cos^2 x \, dx = 1/4 \int \sin^2 2x \, dx \quad \text{(by a)}$$
$$= 1/4 \int \frac{1 - \cos 4x}{2} \, dx \quad \text{(by b)}$$
$$= 1/8 \cdot 1/4 \int (1 - \cos 4x) \, d4x$$
$$= \frac{x}{8} - \frac{\sin 4x}{32} + C \, .$$

(iii)

$$\int \sin^4 x \, dx = \int \frac{(1 - \cos 2x)^2}{2} \, dx \quad \text{(by b)}$$
$$= \int \frac{1}{4} \, dx - \int \frac{\cos 2x}{2} \, dx + \int \frac{\cos^2 2x \, dx}{4}$$
$$= \frac{x}{4} - \frac{\sin 2x}{4} + \int \frac{1 + \cos 4x}{4 \cdot 2} \, dx$$
$$= \frac{x}{4} - \frac{\sin 2x}{4} + \frac{x}{8} + \frac{\sin 4x}{32} + C \, .$$

(Another method involves use of the identity $\sec^2 A = 1 + \tan^2 A$.)

(iv)

$$\int \tan^4 x \, dx = \int (\sec^2 x - 1) \tan^2 x \, dx$$
$$= \int \sec^2 x \cdot \tan^2 x \, dx - \int \tan^2 x \, dx$$
$$= \int \tan^2 x \, d \tan x - \int (\sec^2 x - 1) \, dx$$
$$= \frac{\tan^3 x}{3} - \tan x + x + C.$$

Problems

1. Anti-differentiate with respect to x:

(a) $\sin^2 x$,

(b) $\cos^4 x \sin^4 x$,

(c) $1/\cos x$,

(d) $\cos^4 x$,

(e) $1/(1 + \sin x)$,

(f) $\sin^3 x$,

(g) $\sec^3 x \tan^3 x$,

(h) $\sin^2 x \cos x$,

(i) $\tan^4 x$,

(j) $\cos^4 x \sin^3 x$,

(k) $\cos^3 (a + bx)$,

(l) $\sin^2 x \cos^2 x$,

(m) $\sin^4 x \cos^2 x$,

(n) $\cos^3 x / \sin^4 x$,

(o) $\sin^3 x / \cos^2 x$.

2. *Derive* (do not simply verify) the formulas:

(a) $\int \sec x \, dx = \ln|\sec x + \tan x|$

(b) $\int \csc x \, dx = \ln|\csc x - \cot x|$

3. Anti-differentiate with respect to x:

(a) $\sin mx \cos nx$

(b) $\sin mx \sin nx$

4. Anti-differentiate with respect to x:

(a) $\dfrac{1}{4 + 5 \cos x}$

(b) $\dfrac{1}{1 + \sin x + \cos x}$

5.10 Square Roots of Quadratics

Anti-derivatives involving $\sqrt{(ax^2 + bx + c)}$ can often be handled by a change of variable, which reduces $ax^2 + bx + c$ to a perfect square in terms of the new variable. The substitutions most frequently applied make use of the trigonometric identities (1) $\sin^2 A + \cos^2 A = 1$ and (2) $\sec^2 A = 1 + \tan^2 A$.

Examples

To evaluate $\int \dfrac{1}{x\sqrt{(x^2-1)}}\,dx$, set $x = \sec t$. Then

$$\sqrt{(x^2-1)} = \sqrt{(\sec^2 t - 1)} = \sqrt{(\tan^2 t)} = \tan t \text{ (assuming } \tan t > 0).$$

Also, $dx = \sec t \cdot \tan t\, dt$. (*Exercise:* prove $D_x \sec x = \sec x \tan x$.) Hence the anti-derivative becomes

$$\int \frac{\sec t \cdot \tan t}{\sec t \cdot \tan t}\,dt = \int (1)\,dt = t + C = \sec^{-1} x + C.$$

To find $\int \sqrt{(a^2 - x^2)}\,dx$, set $x = a \sin t$. Then

$$\sqrt{(a^2 - x^2)} = \sqrt{(a^2 - a^2 \sin^2 t)} = a \cos t \quad \text{(assuming } a \cos t > 0).$$

Also $dx = a \cos t\, dt$. Hence the anti-derivative becomes

$$\int a \cos t \cdot a \cos t\, dt = a^2 \int \cos^2 t\, dt$$

$$= a^2 \int \frac{1 + \cos 2t}{2}\,dt$$

$$= \frac{a^2 t}{2} + \frac{a^2 \sin 2t}{4} + C$$

$$= \frac{a^2}{2} \sin^{-1} \frac{x}{a} + \frac{a^2}{4} \cdot 2 \frac{x}{a} \frac{\sqrt{(a^2 - x^2)}}{a} + C$$

$$= \frac{a^2}{2} \sin^{-1} \frac{x}{a} + \frac{x}{2} \sqrt{(a^2 - x^2)} + C.$$

In a case such as $\sqrt{[(x-4)^2 + 9]}$ we would set $(x-4) = 3 \tan t$.

Problem

1. Anti-differentiate with respect to x by trigonometric substitutions:

(a) $\dfrac{1}{(x^2+1)^2}$,

(b) $\dfrac{1}{\sqrt{(-2x - x^2)}}$,

(c) $x^3 \sqrt{(25 + x^2)}$,

(d) $\dfrac{1}{x^2 \sqrt{(25x^2 + 16)}}$,

(e) $\dfrac{1}{x^3 \sqrt{(x^2 - 5)}}$,

(f) $\dfrac{\sqrt{(9 - 4x^2)}}{x}$.

5.11 Trigonometric Reduction Formulas

$\int \sin^n x\, dx$ is expressible in terms of known functions and $\int \sin^{n-2} x\, dx$; by repeatedly reducing the exponent by 2, it can be expressed in terms of known functions and $\int \sin^2 x\, dx$ (if n is even) or $\int \sin x\, dx$ (if n is odd), both of which are known. This is proved as follows:

$$\int \sin^n x\, dx = -\int \sin^{n-1} x\, d\cos x$$

$$= -\cos x \cdot \sin^{n-1} x + \int \cos x\, d\sin^{n-1} x$$

$$= -\cos x \cdot \sin^{n-1} x + (n-1) \int \cos^2 x\, \sin^{n-2} x\, dx$$

$$= -\cos x \cdot \sin^{n-1} x + (n-1) \int (1-\sin^2 x)\, \sin^{n-2} x\, dx$$

$$= -\cos x \cdot \sin^{n-1} x + (n-1) \int \sin^{n-2} x\, dx - (n-1) \int \sin^n x\, dx.$$

Solving for $\int \sin^n x\, dx$, we get

$$\int \sin^n x\, dx = \frac{-\cos x \cdot \sin^{n-1} x}{n} + \frac{n-1}{n} \int \sin^{n-2} x\, dx \qquad (1)$$

as required. By reading this formula in reverse we can express $\int \sin^{n-2} x\, dx$ in terms of $\int \sin^n x\, dx$. This is useful in cases such as $\int (\sin x)^{-4}\, dx$, where we wish to raise the power.

By similar methods, a reduction formula for $\int \sin^n x \cos^m x\, dx$ can be obtained.

These reduction formulas are particularly useful when one wants to integrate from 0 to π, or 0 to $\pi/2$, etc. The calculation then simplifies, for example, as follows:

$$\int_0^{\pi/2} \sin^7 x\, dx = \int \sin^7 x\, dx \,\Big|_0^{\pi/2}$$

$$= \frac{-\cos x \cdot \sin^6 x}{7}\Big|_0^{\pi/2} + 6/7 \int \sin^5 x\, dx \,\Big|_0^{\pi/2} \qquad \text{by (1)}$$

$$= 0 + \frac{6}{7} \cdot \frac{4}{5} \cdot \frac{2}{3} \cdot 1 \qquad \text{(by repetition).}$$

Exercise

1. Derive reduction formulas for $\int \cos^n x\, dx$ and $\int \dfrac{1}{\cos^n x}\, dx$.

5.12 Hyperbolic Functions

The expressions $(e^x + e^{-x})/2$ and $(e^x - e^{-x})/2$ occur so frequently in applications that it has been found convenient to give them special names. In view of the fact that they have properties closely resembling those of $\cos x$ and $\sin x$, only being connected with a hyperbola in the same way that the latter are with a circle, they are called the *hyperbolic cosine* of x and the *hyperbolic sine* of x, respectively—in symbols,

$$\cosh x = \frac{e^x + e^{-x}}{2}, \qquad \sinh x = \frac{e^x - e^{-x}}{2}.$$

Some of the properties referred to are the following: $D_x \cosh x = \sinh x$, $D_x \sinh x = \cosh x$, $\cosh(-x) = \cosh x$, $\sinh(-x) = -\sinh x$, $\cosh^2 x - \sinh^2 x = 1$ (all easily proven). The last equation implies that the locus of $x = \cosh t$, $y = \sinh t$ is the *hyperbola* $x^2 - y^2 = 1$.

We introduce these functions of x here because they are useful in anti-differentiation.

To sketch their graphs we note that $\cosh 0 = 1$ and that $D_x^2 \cosh x = \cosh x > 0$; hence its graph is as shown in Fig. 5-3. We arrive at the graph of $\sinh x$ by noting that $\sinh 0 = 0$ and that $D_x \sinh x = \cosh x$ (Fig. 5-4). We also use the above-mentioned properties that $\cosh(-x) = \cosh x$ and $\sinh(-x) = -\sinh x$.

It is easily seen that $\cosh x - \sinh x$ is always positive and approaches 0 as x tends to infinity; thus the two curves very nearly coincide for large positive values of x. (*Exercise:* prove this.)

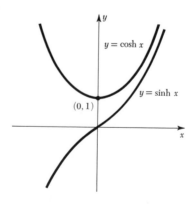

Fig. 5-3

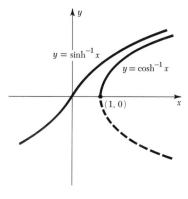

Fig. 5-4

By methods exactly similar to those used for $\sin^{-1} x$, $\cos^{-1} x$ one proves that

$$D_x \sinh^{-1} x = \frac{1}{\sqrt{(1+x^2)}}, \quad D_x \cosh^{-1} x = \frac{1}{\sqrt{(x^2-1)}}.$$

(*Exercise:* give the details of these proofs.) Note that $\cosh^{-1} x$ is taken to be the *positive* number whose cosh is x.

These yield the very useful anti-differentiation formulas

$$\int \frac{1}{\sqrt{(1+x^2)}} dx = \sinh^{-1} x, \ \int \frac{1}{\sqrt{(x^2-1)}} dx = \cosh^{-1} x.$$

The inverse functions can be expressed in terms of logarithms, since by solving

$$x = \frac{e^y - e^{-y}}{2}$$

for y in terms of x, one gets

$$2x = e^y - e^{-y},$$

$$2xe^y = e^{2y} - 1 \quad \text{(a quadratic in } e^y\text{)},$$

$$(e^y)^2 - 2xe^y - 1 = 0.$$

Hence

$$e^y = \frac{+2x \pm \sqrt{4x^2 + 4}}{2}$$

$$= x \pm \sqrt{x^2 + 1}.$$

Since e^y must be positive, we use only the "+" sign, hence

$$e^y = x + \sqrt{x^2 + 1}$$

and

$$y = \ln\left(x + \sqrt{x^2 + 1}\right).$$

By similar methods one gets

$$\cosh^{-1} x = \ln\left(x + \sqrt{x^2 - 1}\right).$$

(*Exercise:* prove this.)

One also gets results resembling those for $\tan x$, $\tan^{-1} x$ on using $\tanh x$ for $\sinh x/\cosh x$, and similarly for $\coth x$, $\operatorname{sech} x$, $\operatorname{cosch} x$. For example,

$$D_x \tanh x = 1 - \tanh^2 x, \ D_x \tanh^{-1} x = \frac{1}{1-x^2}, \ \int \frac{1}{1-x^2}\, dx = \tanh^{-1} x + C.$$

The important anti-derivative $\int \sqrt{(1+x^2)}\, dx$ is most conveniently worked out as follows:

(i)

$$\int \sqrt{(1+x^2)}\, dx = x\sqrt{(1+x^2)} - \int x\, d\sqrt{(1+x^2)} \quad \text{(by parts)}$$

$$= x\sqrt{(1+x^2)} - \int \frac{x^2}{\sqrt{(1+x^2)}}\, dx$$

$$= x\sqrt{(1+x^2)} - \int \frac{1+x^2-1}{\sqrt{(1+x^2)}}\, dx$$

$$= x\sqrt{(1+x^2)} - \int \sqrt{(1+x^2)}\, dx + \int \frac{1}{\sqrt{(1+x^2)}}\, dx.$$

Therefore

$$\int \sqrt{(1+x^2)}\, dx = \frac{x}{2}\sqrt{(1+x^2)} + \frac{1}{2}\int \frac{1}{\sqrt{(1+x^2)}}\, dx$$

$$= \frac{x}{2}\sqrt{(1+x^2)} + \frac{1}{2}\sinh^{-1} x + C.$$

As additional examples, we have

(ii)

$$\int \frac{1}{\sqrt{x^2 + 2x - 3}}\, dx = \int \frac{1}{\sqrt{(x+1)^2 - 4}}\, dx$$

$$= \int \frac{1 \cdot 2}{2\sqrt{\left(\frac{x+1}{2}\right)^2 - 1}} \, d\frac{x+1}{2}$$

$$= \cosh^{-1} \frac{x+1}{2} + C.$$

(*Exercise:* proceed also by setting $x+1 = 2 \cosh y$.)
  (iii)

$$\int \frac{2}{\sqrt{(2x+4)^2 + 1}} \, dx = \int \frac{1}{\sqrt{(2x+4)^2 + 1}} \, d(2x+4)$$

$$= \sinh^{-1}(2x+4) + C.$$

(*Exercise:* proceed also by substitution.)

Problems

1. Prove:
   (a) $\sinh(x-y) = \sinh x \cosh y - \cosh x \sinh y$,
   (b) $\tanh(x+y) = \dfrac{\tanh x + \tanh y}{1 + \tanh x \tanh y}$,
   (c) $\sinh x + \sinh y = 2 \sinh \dfrac{x+y}{2} \cosh \dfrac{x-y}{2}$,
   (d) $d \tanh x = (1 - \tanh^2 x) \, dx$,
   (e) $\int \dfrac{1}{1-x^2} \, dx = \tanh^{-1} x + C$.

2. Find anti-derivatives with respect to x using hyperbolic functions:
   (a) $1/(4 - 5x^2)$,   (b) $1/\sqrt{(4x^2 - 1)}$,
   (c) $1/\sqrt{(a^2 + b^2 x^2)}$,   (d) $e^x \sinh x$.

3. Find anti-derivatives with respect to x using substitutions which elimi-
   nate fractional powers:

   (a) $\dfrac{1}{x^{1/2} - 1}$,   (b) $\dfrac{x^{1/3}}{2x^{1/2} - x^{1/3}}$,
   (c) $\dfrac{x^{1/2}}{x^{1/3} - 2x^{1/2}}$.

5.13 The Solving of Differential Equations

The evaluation of $\int f(x) \, dx$ amounts to solving the equation $D_x y = f(x)$, or more conveniently for our present purpose, $D_t y / D_t x = f(x)$, for y as a function of x (t being an arbitrarily chosen para-meter). Equations involving derivatives of the unknown functions are called *differential equations*, and solving such equations may be regarded as a generalization of the problem of anti-differentiation.

In the subsequent operations the "t" subscripts are carried along unaltered, so we will leave them understood.

Examples

(i)

$$\frac{Dy}{Dx} = x^2 \cdot y.$$

This is of a type known as "variables separable," in which the x's and y's can be immediately separated out. Doing this gives

$$\frac{1}{y} Dy = x^2 Dx.$$

Hence $D^{-1} 1/y\, Dy = D^{-1} x^2\, Dx$, and (see Section 5.2) these expressions can be evaluated as anti-derivatives:

$$\ln|y| = \frac{x^3}{3} + C \qquad (C \text{ an arbitrary constant}),$$

$$|y| = e^{x^3/3} \cdot e^C = K\, e^{x^3/3} \qquad (K \text{ an arbitrary positive} \atop \text{constant}).$$

(ii)

$$\frac{Dy}{Dx} = \frac{x+y}{x-y}.$$

The expression on the right side is unaltered if x and y are replaced by $k \cdot x$ and $k \cdot y$. Such a case is known as *homogeneous*. The right side can be written as

$$\frac{1 + y/x}{1 - y/x},$$

which involves the single variable y/x, denoted "v", say, and this suggests trying to find v in terms of x.

$$\frac{y}{x} = v \quad \text{gives} \quad y = vx,$$

and hence $Dy = v\,Dx + x\,Dv$. Thus the given differential equation amounts to

$$\frac{v\,Dx + x\,Dv}{Dx} = \frac{1+v}{1-v},$$

that is,

$$v + x\frac{Dv}{Dx} = \frac{1+v}{1-v},$$

in which the variables separate as follows:

$$x\frac{Dv}{Dx} = \frac{1+v}{1-v} - v = \frac{1+v-v+v^2}{1-v},$$

$$\frac{1-v}{1+v^2}Dv = \frac{1}{x}Dx.$$

Hence, applying D^{-1} to both sides and using Section 5.2,

$$\int\frac{1-v}{1+v^2}dv = \int\frac{1}{x}dx$$

(these anti-differentiations are left as exercises).

Replacing v by y/x gives the required connection between x and y. One could have proceeded throughout by using $D_x y$ instead of Dy/Dx, but the manipulations would have been more clumsy. For example, in (i),

$$D_x y = x^2 \cdot y,$$

$$\frac{1}{x^2 y} \cdot D_x y = 1,$$

$$\frac{1}{x^2}D_x \ln|y| = 1,$$

$$\frac{1}{D_x x^3/3} \cdot D_x \ln|y| = 1,$$

$$D_{x^3/3} \ln|y| = 1,$$

$$\ln|y| = \frac{x^3}{3} + C.$$

The use of the chain rule, as incorporated in the D notation, makes for much greater neatness of expression.

The equations in (i) and (ii) are often written as

$$x^2 \cdot y \, Dx - Dy = 0 \quad \text{and} \quad (x+y)\, Dx - (x-y)\, Dy = 0,$$

thus anticipating the separation of variables.

In equations such as $2D_x{}^2 y - 3D_x y + y = e^x$ where derivatives of higher order are involved, the subscript x is also often left out. Thus one sees

$$2D^2 y - 3Dy + y = e^x.$$

Here the omitted subscript must be understood to be x, however. The omitted subscript in writing Dy/Dx for $D_x y$ is immaterial because of the chain rule, but no such rule is available for higher order derivatives. We shall not solve such equations here.

Applying the solution of a differential equation generally involves two things—getting the general form of the relationship between the variables and determining the values of the parameters involved in order to fit the particular facts given. The following exercise illustrates this.

(iii) Radium decomposes at a rate proportional to the amount present, and half of a given quantity decomposes in 1600 years. What proportion is left after 100 years?

The equation describing the general law is

$$\frac{DR}{Dt} = kR,$$

where R is a function of t, being the amount present at time t, and K is a constant. Here the variables separate, giving

$$\frac{1}{R} DR = k\, Dt,$$

$$D^{-1} \frac{1}{R} DR = D^{-1} k\, Dt \qquad \text{(anti-differentiating)},$$

$$\ln R = kt + C \qquad \text{(being a constant)},$$

$$R = e^{Kt+C}$$

$$= e^{Kt} \cdot e^{C},$$

which is the general form of the required relationship, involving two parameters, K and C.

We have so far, however, used only the fact that "radium decomposes at a rate proportional to the amount present." Let us try to choose K and C to make the solution fit the two conditions (a) an amount M is initially present, and (b) half a given quantity decomposes in 1600 years.

(a) says that $R = M$ when $t = 0$. This gives $M = e^0 \cdot e^C$, and hence $e^C = M$. Thus the equation is $R = e^{Kt} \cdot M$. (b) says that $R = M/2$ when $t = 1600$. This gives $M/2 = e^{1600K} M$. Hence

$$\frac{1}{2} = e^{1600K},$$

$$\ln \frac{1}{2} = 1600K,$$

$$K = \frac{1}{1600} \ln \frac{1}{2}.$$

Thus the equation is

$$R = e^{1/1600 \ln 1/2\, t} \cdot M$$

$$= (e^{\ln 1/2})^{t/1600} \cdot M$$

$$= \left(\frac{1}{2}\right)^{t/1600} M.$$

To answer the given question, we put $t = 100$. This gives

$$R_{100} = \left(\frac{1}{2}\right)^{100/1600} M$$

$$= \left(\frac{1}{2}\right)^{1/16} M.$$

The proportion left is thus

$$\frac{\left(\frac{1}{2}\right)^{1/16} M}{M} = \left(\frac{1}{2}\right)^{1/16}$$

$$= 96\% \text{ (approximately)}.$$

Problems

1. Solve the following differential equations:

   (a) $x(y^2 - 9) + y(1 + x) D_x y = 0$,
   (b) $4x^2 D_x y = 1 + y^2$,
   (c) $D_x y + e^y \cos x = 0$,
   (d) $y + 1 + (x - 3) D_x y = 0$,
   (e) $D_\theta r + \dfrac{r^2 + 1}{r \sin \theta} \cos \theta = 0$,
   (f) $y^2 + xy + 3x^2 D_x y = 0$,
   (g) $2x - 5y + 2 + (10y - 4x) D_x y = 0$,
   (h) $x^2 - xy + y^2 - xy\, D_x y = 0$,
   (i) $xy - (x^2 + 2y^2) D_x y = 0$,
   (j) $xD_x y - \left(y + x \tan \dfrac{y}{x}\right) = 0$.

2. A tank contains G gallons of brine in which are dissolved S pounds of salt. Water is run into the tank at R gallons per minute and is run out at the same rate, the mixture being stirred continually. How much salt is in the tank after M minutes?

3. We are given that the acceleration due to gravity of an object at a distance r from the center of the earth is K/r^2, K being a constant. We are also given that the earth's radius is R and that the acceleration due to gravity at the surface is $-g$. Prove that the velocity v satisifies the differential equation

$$v\,D_r v = -g\frac{R^2}{r^2}.$$

If a projectile is fired upward with a velocity v_0, express its velocity in terms of its distance r from the center of the earth. For what initial velocities v_0 will it never return to the earth? (Under what conditions can the equation continue to hold as $r \to \infty$?)

4. The proportion of incident light absorbed by a thin layer of glass is proportional to its thickness. If 1 inch of glass absorbs 1/2 of the incident light, what thickness absorbs 7/8 of the incident light?

6

Applications of the Definite Integral

Definite integrals are usually evaluated by means of the Fundamental Theorem, which reduces the problem to that of anti-differentiation. Now that we have dealt with some of the more common techniques of anti-differentiation, we are in a position to consider a variety of applications of the definite integral.

First we give a number of useful properties of definite integrals generally.

6.1 Properties of the Definite Integral

(a)

$$\int_a^b f(x)\ dx = -\int_b^a f(x)\ dx.$$

This can be seen directly from the definition of the definite integral (Section 4.3) by noting that if the same points x_i of subdivision are used for both integrals, the same Δx's are obtained, only with a change of sign, since the points are labeled in opposite directions.

The Fundamental Theorem also yields a proof, since

$$F(x)\Big|_a^b = -F(x)\Big|_b^a .$$

(b)

$$\int_a^b f(x)\ dx = \int_a^c f(x)\ dx + \int_c^b f(x)\ dx.$$

109

If $a < c < b$, the subdivisions for (a,c), (c,b) yield a subdivision for (a,b), and the result follows from

$$\sum_a^b f(x) \, \Delta x = \sum_a^c f(x) \, \Delta x + \sum_c^b f(x) \, \Delta x$$

on taking limits. In other cases (for example, $a < b < c$) there is overlapping, but the extra contributions [for example, from (b,c), (c,b)] have opposite signs and cancel.

The Fundamental Theorem gives a proof, since

$$F(x)\Big|_a^b = F(x)\Big|_a^c + F(x)\Big|_c^b.$$

(c)
$$\int_a^b K \cdot f(x) \, dx = K \int_a^b f(x) \, dx$$

(the proof is left to the reader).

(d) If $f(x)$ is positive (negative) throughout (a,b), where $a < b$, then $\int_a^b f(x) \, dx$ is positive (negative). (The proof is left to the reader.)

(e) Change of variable: If $x = p(t)$ and t_a, t_b are values of t corresponding to $x = a$, $x = b$, respectively, then

$$\int_a^b f(x) \, dx = \int_{t_a}^{t_b} f[p(t)] \, p'(t) \, dt. \tag{1}$$

Thus (provided one replaces the limits for x by the corresponding limits for t), one can interchange within the symbol for a definite integral the symbols "dx," or "$dp(t)$," and "$p'(t)dt$."

Recall the similar result of Section 5.3. Formula (1) can be regarded as a chain rule of integral calculus. Note its resemblance to the chain rule of anti-differentiation. Both it and the usual chain rule follow from the identity

$$\Delta x = \frac{\Delta x}{\Delta t} \cdot \Delta t.$$

The chain rule for differentiation follows on dividing by Δu (u being the other variable involved), getting

$$\frac{\Delta x}{\Delta u} = \frac{\Delta x}{\Delta t} \cdot \frac{\Delta t}{\Delta u}$$

and thence

$$D_u x = D_t x \cdot D_u t,$$

on letting Δu, Δx, Δt approach 0.

The change of variable rule for integration follows on multiplying by $f(x)$ (for each little interval), getting

$$f(x) \, \Delta x = f(x) \cdot \frac{\Delta x}{\Delta t} \cdot \Delta t$$

and thence

$$\int_a^b f(x) \, dx = \int_{t_b}^{t_b} f(x) \, D_t x \cdot dt,$$

on summing and letting the norm δ of the decomposition approach 0. (The details of this proof, involving the law of the mean, we omit.) It also follows from the Fundamental Theorem and the chain rule of anti-differentiation, since

$$\int f(x) \, dx = \int f(x) \, D_t x \, dt,$$

and substituting a, b for x, and then subtracting, gives the same value as using t_a, t_b for t.

It is also to be noted that this rule implies the Fundamental Theorem, for if $F'(x) = f(x)$, then

$$\int_a^b f(x) \, dx = \int_{x=a}^{x=b} 1 \cdot dF(x),$$

which is obviously $F(b) - F(a)$ (think of the definition of the integral). Thus, we could have proceeded by proving our rule directly (the proof resembling that of the Fundamental Theorem, using the law of the mean) and then deriving the Fundamental Theorem from it.

One necessary precaution is that $p(t)$ must not inadvertently be taken to be multiple-valued over the interval concerned. For example, if in working out $\int_{-1}^{1} 1 \cdot dx$ one puts $x^{2/3} = t$, this yields $t = +1, +1$ for $x = -1, +1$, and since $x = t^{3/2}$ one might try to use $\int_1^1 1 \cdot 3/2 \, t^{1/2} \, dt$. But this is 0, whereas the original integral has value 2. The error lies in the fact that $t^{3/2}$ is double-valued. If one uses $-\sqrt{(t^3)}$ as x varies from -1 to 0, but $+\sqrt{t^3}$ while x varies from 0 to $+1$, splitting the integral into two parts, the correct value is obtained.

(f) Integration by parts: The "by parts" method of anti-differentiation yields a corresponding integration formula.

$$\int_{x=a}^b f(x) \, dg(x) = \int f(x) \, dg(x) \Big|_{x=a}^b \qquad \text{(Fundamental Theorem)}$$

$$= \left[f(x) \cdot g(x) - \int g(x) \, df(x) \right]_a^b$$

$$= f(x) \cdot g(x) \Big|_a^b - \int_a^b g(x) \, df(x) \qquad \text{(Fundamental Theorem)}.$$

This equation has a simple geometrical interpretation in terms of the graph obtained by plotting $g(x)$ against $f(x)$. In Fig. 6-1, this is the arc from A to B. It is the locus of $[f(x),g(x)]$ as x varies from a to b. (Area of large rectangle $=f(b)\cdot g(b)$. The other areas are as shown.) By adding and subtracting areas,

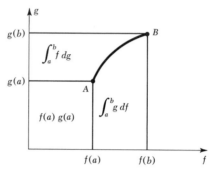

Fig. 6-1

$$\int_a^b f\,dg = f(b)\cdot g(b) - f(a)\cdot g(a) - \int_a^b g\,df.$$

6.2 Notation

In evaluating a definite integral we have our choice of two notations. We may either quote the Fundamental Theorem immediately, getting

$$\int_a^b f(x)\,dx = \int f(x)\,dx \bigg|_a^b$$

and continue to find an anti-derivative as in the last chapter, or we may use the above rules, usually applying the Fundamental Theorem only at the very end when an anti-derivative is obvious. The manipulations run exactly parallel. For example, consider

$$\int_1^2 \frac{\ln x}{x}\,dx \qquad\qquad = \qquad \int \frac{\ln x}{x}\,dx\bigg|_1^2$$

$$= \int_{x=1}^2 \ln x\,d\ln x \qquad\qquad = \int \ln x\,d\ln x\bigg|_1^2$$

$$= \int_{x=1}^2 1\,d\frac{(\ln x)^2}{2} \qquad\qquad = \int d\frac{(\ln x)^2}{2}\bigg|_1^2$$

$$= \frac{(\ln x)^2}{2}\bigg|_1^2. \qquad\qquad = \frac{(\ln x)^2}{2}\bigg|_1^2.$$

Note the usefulness of our anti-differentiation notation in paralleling the definite integral notation. This makes for a carry-over of technique. We will follow the usual custom by remaining within the definite integral notation.

The rest of this chapter is devoted to showing how definite integrals may be used in problems involving lengths, areas, volumes, pressure, work, moments of inertia, mean values, and centroids.

6.3 Arc Length

Cartesian coordinates. The length of an arc (see Fig. 6-2) is defined

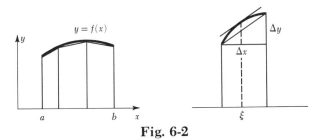

Fig. 6-2

as follows: take points along the arc and join them by straight line segments; then the limit of the sum of the lengths of all these segments, as the corresponding subdivision of (a,b) gets finer and finer, is defined to be the *length* of the arc. The length of a typical segment is

$$\sqrt{(\Delta x)^2 + (\Delta y)^2} = \sqrt{1 + \left(\frac{\Delta y}{\Delta x}\right)^2}\, \Delta x.$$

But, by the law of the mean, the slope $\Delta y/\Delta x$ of the chord is $f'\,(\xi)$ for some ξ inside the interval Δx. Hence

$$\text{arc length} = \lim_{\delta \to 0} \sum_a^b \sqrt{1 + (f'\,(\xi))^2}\, \Delta x$$

$$= \int_a^b \sqrt{1 + [f'\,(x)]^2}\, dx.$$

Polar coordinates. If $\Delta\rho$, $\Delta\theta$ are little increments in ρ and θ corresponding to a small segment Δs of arc, then the arcs corresponding to $\Delta\rho$, $\rho\Delta\theta$, Δs are all very nearly straight, forming a right-angled triangle, very nearly (Fig. 6-3). This "triangle" gives

$$\Delta s = \sqrt{(\Delta\rho)^2 + (\rho\Delta\theta)^2} \quad \text{(approximately)}$$

$$= \sqrt{\left(\frac{\Delta\rho}{\Delta\theta}\right)^2 + \rho^2}\, \Delta\theta.$$

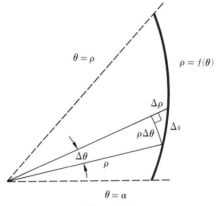

Fig. 6-3

Thus, on summing and taking the limit, we suspect that the arc length from $\theta = \alpha$ to β is

$$\int_\alpha^\beta \sqrt{(D_\theta \rho)^2 + \rho^2} \, d\theta .$$

A more respectable proof is got by using the above result for Cartesian coordinates and changing into polar form by using the equations

$$x = \rho \cos \theta ,$$

$$y = \rho \sin \theta , \qquad (\text{where } \rho = f(\theta)) .$$

$$\text{Arc length} = \int_a^b \sqrt{1 + (D_x y)^2} \, dx$$

$$= \int_\alpha^\beta \sqrt{1 + \left(\frac{\rho \cos \theta + \rho' \sin \theta}{-\rho \sin \theta + \rho' \cos \theta} \right)^2} \cdot (-\rho \sin \theta + \rho' \cos \theta) \, d\theta ,$$

which simplifies as required.

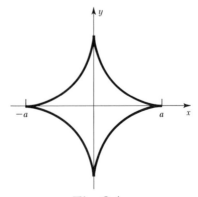

Fig. 6-4

(i) In Fig. 6-4, the total arc length of the curve

$$x^{2/3} + y^{2/3} = a^{2/3}$$

is

$$4 \int_0^a \sqrt{1 + (D_x y)^2} \, dx.$$

$(D_x y)^2$ reduces to

$$\frac{a^{2/3} - x^{2/3}}{x^{2/3}} = \frac{a^{2/3}}{x^{2/3}} - 1.$$

The integral hence becomes

$$4 \int_0^a \sqrt{\frac{a^{2/3}}{x^{2/3}}} \, dx$$

$$= 4 \int_0^a \frac{a^{1/3}}{x^{1/3}} \, dx = 6a.$$

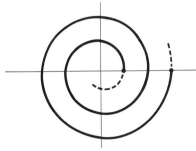

Fig. 6-5

(ii) In Fig. 6-5, the arc length of $\rho = e^\theta$ from $\theta = 0$ to $\theta = 4\pi$ is

$$\int_0^{4\pi} \sqrt{(D_\theta \rho)^2 + \rho^2} \, d\theta$$

$$= \int_0^{4\pi} \sqrt{(e^{2\theta} + e^{2\theta})} \, d\theta$$

$$= \sqrt{2} \, (e^{4\pi} - 1).$$

Parametric equations. If the curve is given parametrically in the form $x = f(t)$, $y = g(t)$, then

$$\int_a^b \sqrt{(1 + (D_x y)^2)} \, dx = \int_{t_a}^{t_b} \sqrt{\left(1 + \left(\frac{g'(t)}{f'(t)}\right)^2\right)} \, f'(t) \, dt$$

$$= \int_{t_a}^{t_b} \sqrt{[f'(t)]^2 + [g'(t)^2]} \, dt.$$

Exercises

Find the following arc lengths:

1. Along $y = \ln \sec x$ from $x = 0$ to $x = \dfrac{\pi}{3}$.

2. Along $y = \cosh x$ from $x = 0$ to $x = k$.

3. Along $y = \ln (1 - x^2)$ from $x = 0$ to $x = \dfrac{1}{2}$.

4. Along $\rho = a\theta$ from $\theta = 0$ to $\theta = 2\pi$ (ρ, θ being polar coordinates).

Problems

Find the arc lengths of the following:

5. One arch of a cycloid generated by a circle of radius a.

6. The total circumference of $\rho = 1 + \cos \theta$.

7. The arc of $\rho = \dfrac{2}{1 + \cos \theta}$ from $\theta = 0$ to $\theta = \pi/2$.

8. The arc given by parametric equations $x = \cos \theta + \theta \sin \theta$, $y = \sin \theta - \theta \cos \theta$ from $\theta = 0$ to $\theta = \pi/2$.

9. The total circumference of $\rho = a (1 + \sin \theta)$.

10. The arc given by parametric equations $x = a \cos^3 t$, $y = a \sin^3 t$.

11. The arc with parametric equations $x = e^{-t} \cos t$, $y = e^{-t} \sin t$, from $t = 0$ to $t = \pi$.

12. The arc with parametric equations $x = 2 (2t + 3)^{3/2}$, $y = 3 (t + 1)^2$ from $t = 1$ to $t = 3$.

6.4 Area

Cartesian coordinates. The basic result appears in Section 4.1. More complex examples are handled by expressing the given area in terms of those of regions of this simple type.

Polar coordinates. In Fig. 6-6, the problem is to find the area bounded by the straight lines $\theta = \alpha$, $\theta = \beta$ and the curve $\rho = f(\theta)$. Doing to ρ, θ what we previously did with y, x gives a subdivision as shown. The area of a typical circular sector is $\rho^2/2 \cdot \Delta\theta$, and the limit of the sum of these is $\displaystyle\int_{\alpha}^{\beta} \rho^2/2 \, d\theta$.

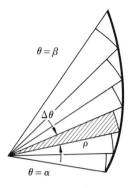

Fig. 6-6

Parametric equations. Parametric representation is particularly convenient for dealing with closed curves. In Fig. 6-7, suppose

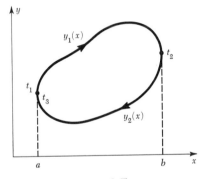

Fig. 6-7

that as t varies from t_1 to t_2 to t_3, the point $[x=f(t), y=g(t)]$ completes the indicated circuit *clockwise* exactly once, and that we wish to know the enclosed area. Let the (ordinary) equations of the "top" of the curve (described as t varies from t_1 to t_2) and "bottom" of the curve (t varies from t_2 to t_3) be $y=y_1(x)$, $y=y_2(x)$ respectively. [y is always $g(t)$, however.] The required area is clearly

$$\int_a^b y_1(x)\,dx - \int_a^b y_2(x)\,dx$$

(the area under the upper part
of the curve minus the area
under the lower part)

$$= \int_{t_1}^{t_2} g(t)\,df(t) - \int_{t_3}^{t_2} g(t)\,df(t) \tag{1}$$

$$= \int_{t_1}^{t_2} g(t) f'(t) \, dt - \int_{t_3}^{t_2} g(t) f'(t) \, dt$$

$$= \int_{t_1}^{t_2} g(t) f'(t) \, dt + \int_{t_2}^{t_3} g(t) f'(t) \, dt$$

$$= \int_{t_1}^{t_3} g(t) \cdot f'(t) \, dt .$$

Thus, on integrating from t_1 to t_3, the areas are subtracted automatically. This holds quite generally, even in such cases as that shown in Fig. 6-8. If the curve is described *counterclockwise*,

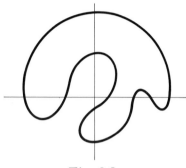

Fig. 6-8

then a minus sign must be introduced in each term, beginning at line (1), the final result being

$$\text{area} = - \int_{t_1}^{t_3} g(t) \cdot f'(t) \, dt .$$

Area of a surface of revolution. Suppose the portion of the curve $y = f(x)$ between $x = a$ and $x = b$ is rotated about the x-axis (Fig. 6-9).

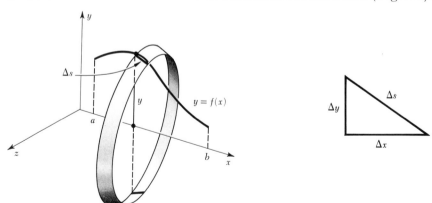

Fig. 6-9

If we approximate to the curve by a polygon (as in finding arc lengths), then each little segment sweeps out a "ribbon" of width Δs and length $2\pi y$, and hence of area (approximately) $2\pi y \Delta s$, where

$$2\pi y \Delta s = 2\pi y \sqrt{1+\left(\frac{\Delta y}{\Delta x}\right)^2}\,\Delta x \qquad \text{(in terms of } x\text{).}$$

This suggests defining the surface area to be

$$\int_a^b 2\pi y \sqrt{1+f'(x)^2}\,dx.$$

[This gives the usual results for simple areas of revolution (conical, cylindrical, etc.) obtained by variations of our limiting argument amounting to more or less disguised integration.]

A natural question to ask is "Why not use the segment Δx instead of Δs?" Will it not give the area also?" The simple case of a line through the origin at an angle of 60° (Fig. 6-10) shows that the results

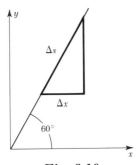

Fig. 6-10

are not the same. Δs is always $2 \cdot \Delta x$ and thus

$$2\pi y \Delta s = 2 \cdot 2\pi y \Delta x.$$

Hence using Δx would give only half the required answer.

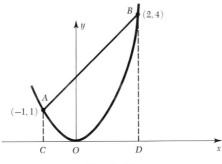

Fig. 6-11

Examples

(i) Let us find the area cut off from the parabola $y=x^2$ by the line $x-y+2=0$ (Fig. 6-11).

Replacing x in the first equation by $y-2$ we get $y=(y-2)^2$, which gives $y^2-5y+4=0$ on simplifying, whence $(y-1)(y-4)=0$. Putting $y=1, 4$ in turn gives $x=-1, 2$, respectively. Thus the curves intersect as shown. The area of the parabolic section AOB is equal to the difference of two areas of "standard shape," namely $ABDC$ and $AOBDC$. The first of these areas is $\int_{-1}^{2}(x+2)\,dx$ and the second is $\int_{-1}^{2}x^2\,dx$. Thus the required area is

$$\int_{-1}^{2}(x+2)\,dx-\int_{-1}^{2}x^2\,dx=\int_{-1}^{2}(x+2-x^2)\,dx$$

$$=\frac{x^2}{2}+2x-\frac{x^3}{3}\Big|_{-1}^{2}$$

$$=4\frac{1}{2}.$$

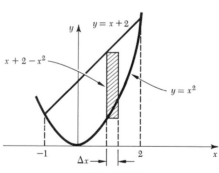

Fig. 6-12

Another approach to the same integral is to think of the region as made up of vertical strips of width Δx and length $x+2-x^2$ (Fig. 6-12). The limit of the sum of the areas of these strips is

$$\int_{-1}^{2}(x+2-x^2)\,dx\,,$$

which is the integral arrived at previously.

(ii) The area inside the cardiod $\rho=1+\cos\theta$ (Fig. 6-13) is

$$2 \int_0^\pi \frac{(1+\cos\theta)^2}{2} \, d\theta$$

$$= \int_0^\pi 1 \, d\theta + \int_0^\pi \cos^2\theta \, d\theta + \int_0^\pi 2\cos\theta \, d\theta$$

$$= \pi + \frac{\pi}{2} + 0 = 3\frac{\pi}{2} \qquad \text{(see Section 5.9).}$$

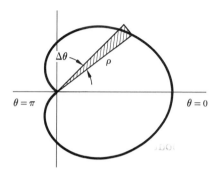

Fig. 6-13

The element of area is $\rho^2/2 \, \Delta\theta$, and as θ varies from 0 to π, the upper half of the region is described from right to left. To get the entire area we must multiply by 2.

(iii) As t varies from 0 to 2π, the point $x = 2 + \cos t$, $y = 3\sin t$ describes the ellipse $(x-2)^2 + (y/3)^2 = 1$ counterclockwise (see Fig. 6-14). We can see this by noting that $x - 2 = \cos t$, $y/3 = \sin t$, and using the identity $\cos^2 t + \sin^2 t = 1$. The area enclosed is (using a minus sign because of the *counterclockwise* description)

$$-\int_0^{2\pi} y \, dx = -\int_0^{2\pi} -3\sin t \, (-\sin t) \, dt$$

$$= 3\int_0^{2\pi} \sin^2 t \, dt = 3\pi \qquad \text{(see Section 5.9).}$$

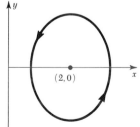

Fig. 6-14

(iv) We can obtain a hemisphere (Fig. 6-15) by rotating a quadrant

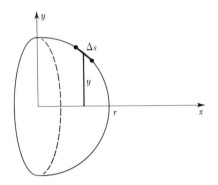

Fig. 6-15

of a circle $x^2 + y^2 = r^2$ about the x-axis. The surface area of the hemisphere is

$$\lim_{\delta \to 0} \sum_0^r 2\pi y \cdot \Delta s = \int_0^r 2\pi \sqrt{(r^2 - x^2)} \sqrt{1 + (D_x y)^2} \, dx.$$

From $x^2 + y^2 = r^2$ we get $2x + 2y D_x y = 0$, hence $D_x y = -x/y$, and the integral becomes

$$\int_0^r 2\pi \sqrt{r^2 - x^2} \sqrt{1 + \frac{x^2}{y^2}} \, dx = 2\pi \int_0^r r \, dx = 2\pi r^2.$$

(The simplification results from the fact that $r^2 - x^2 = y^2$ and $\sqrt{y^2 + x^2} = r$.)

Exercises

Find the following areas:

1. Under one arch of a cycloid $x = a\,(\theta - \sin \theta)$, $y = a\,(1 - \cos \theta)$.

2. Between $y^2 - 2x + 2 = 0$ and $x + y = 5$.

3. Between $x^2 = 8y$ and $x - 2y + 8 = 0$.

4. Between $y = x^2$ and $2x - y + 3 = 0$.

5. Inside $\rho = a \cos \theta$ (polar coordinates).

6. The surface area of a right circular cone of radius a and height h.

Problems

Find the following areas:

7. Inside $x = a \cos^3 t$, $y = a \sin^3 t$.

8. Common to $\rho = \cos \theta$, $\rho = \sin \theta$.

9. Inside $\rho^2 = a^2 \sin \theta$.

10. Inside $\rho = a \sin 2\theta$.

11. Inside $\rho = a \cos \theta$ and outside $\rho = a (1 - \cos \theta)$.

12. Bounded by the coordinate axes and $x = a \cos^4 \theta$, $y = a \sin^4 \theta$.

13. Inside $\rho = p \cos \theta + q \sin \theta$.

14. Inside $\rho = 10 \cos \theta$ and to the right of $\rho \cos \theta = 2$.

15. Generated by revolving one arch of a cycloid $x = a (\theta - \sin \theta)$, $y = a (1 - \cos \theta)$ about the x-axis.

16. Cut off from a sphere of radius r by two parallel planes a distance a apart.

17. Generated by revolving one arch of $y = \sin x$ about the x-axis.

18. Generated by revolving $\rho = a (1 + \cos \theta)$ about the $\theta = 0$ line.

19. Between $y^2 = a^2 + ax$ and $y^2 = a^2 - ax$.

20. Inside the ellipse $x^2/a^2 + y^2/b^2 = 1$.

21. Bounded by $x = 2a$ and $x^2 - y^2 = a^2$.

6.5 Volume

If we know the areas of parallel sections of a solid, then we can find its volume by integration. To see this, think of slicing the solid into thin sections by planes perpendicular to the x-axis (Fig. 6-16). The

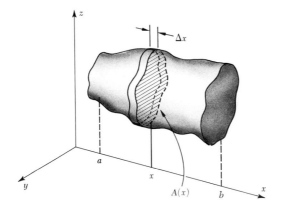

Fig. 6-16

volume of a typical slice will be its section area, $A (x)$, (for some suitable x within it) multiplied by its thickness, Δx—i.e., $A (x) \Delta x$. [Using the biggest section area within the slice will clearly give too big a volume, and using the smallest section area will give too small a volume. Hence some section area $A(x)$, in between, will give the correct volume, $A(x)\,\Delta x$.]

Hence, by limit of sums, the volume $=\displaystyle\int_a^b A(x)\,dx$.

In the case of the solid got by rotating the curve $y=f(x)$ about the x-axis (Fig. 6-17), $A(x)$ is clearly $\pi[f(x)]^2$, since the section is a circle of radius $f(x)$.

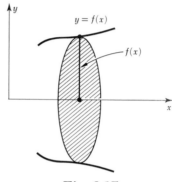

Fig. 6-17

Examples

(i) Volume of hemisphere of radius r (Fig. 6-18).

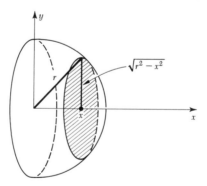

Fig. 6-18

$$=\int_0^r \pi\,(r^2-x^2)\,dx$$

$$=\pi\left(r^2 x-\frac{x^3}{3}\right)\Bigg|_0^r=\frac{2}{3}\,\pi\,r^3.$$

(ii) The base of a solid is bounded by the lines $y=x$, $y=-x$, and $x=1$ (Fig. 6-19). Its cross-sections perpendicular to the x-axis are squares. What is its volume?

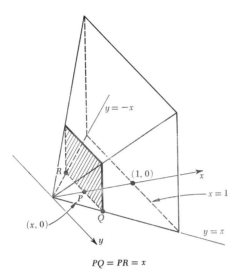

$$PQ = PR = x$$

Fig. 6-19

The section through the point $(x,0)$ is a square of sides $2x$ and hence of area $4x^2$. The required volume is therefore

$$\int_0^1 4x^2 \, dx$$

$$= \frac{4x^3}{3}\Big|_0^1$$

$$= \frac{4}{3}.$$

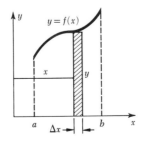

Fig. 6-20

(iii)   In Fig. 6-20, if the region under $y=f(x)$ between $x=a$ and $x=b$ is rotated about the y-axis rather than the x-axis, another method is used—the *cylindrical shell* method (see Fig. 6-21). Using the usual

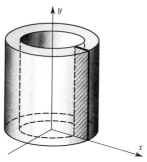

Fig. 6-21

rectangular element of area of dimensions y, Δx we note that it has area $y\Delta x$ and that its inner side travels a distance $2\pi x$. Hence it sweeps out a cylindrical shell of volume approximately equal to $2\pi xy\Delta x$, where $y=f(x)$. (Actually, by considering the volume as the difference of the volumes of two cylinders, its value can be seen to be $2\pi x_1 y$, for $x < x_1 < x+\Delta x$, but the use of x for x_1 has no effect on the result of integration. This is not surprising, for the rectangles get thinner and thinner. A proof can be given, but we shall not give one here.)

On taking the limit of the sum of terms of the form $2\pi xy\Delta x$ we get, finally,

$$\text{volume} = \int_a^b 2\pi x f(x)\, dx.$$

Exercises

Find the following volumes.

1. Generated by revolving an equilateral triangle of side a about a side.

2. Generated by revolving $x^2/a^2 + y^2/b^2 = 1$ about the x-axis.

3. Of the ellipsoid $x^2/a^2 + y^2/b^2 + z^2/c^2 = 1$. (Use the result of Problem 14 of preceding section.)

4. Generated by revolving one arch of the cycloid $x = a\,(\theta - \sin\theta)$, $y = a\,(1 - \cos\theta)$ about the x-axis.

5. Of a solid whose base is bounded by the parabola $y^2 = 4x$ and the line $x = 1$, and whose cross-sections perpendicular to the x-axis are all squares.

6. Of a right circular cone of radius r and height h.

Problems

7. A point P lies at a height h above the plane of a closed region of area A. Find the volume of the cone got by joining P to all points of the boundary of the region.

8. A tree has radius a. A 60° notch is cut, one plane of which is horizontal, the other meeting it on a line through the center of the tree. Find the volume of the wedge.

9. Find the volume inside the surface $x^4/a^4 + y^2/b^2 + z^2/c^2 = 1$.

10. The area bounded by $y^2 - 4y + 2x - 5 = 0$ and the y-axis is rotated about the y-axis. Find the volume generated.

11. The region bounded by $y = \sin x$ and the x-axis from $x = 0$ to $x = \pi$ is rotated about the y-axis. Find the volume swept out.

12. The region bounded by $y = x^2$, $x = 1$, $x = 2$, $y = 0$ is rotated about the y-axis. Find the volume swept out. (Do this by the *cylindrical shell* method: divide the region into vertical strips of height y and width Δx. Each strip when rotated sweeps out a cylindrical shell: approximate to the volume of this shell to get the contribution of each strip, then integrate over the whole region.)

13. A right circular cone is cut by two planes through its axis. Find the volume cut out.

14. Find the volume generated by rotating a circle of radius r about one of its tangents.

15. A wedge is cut from a sphere by two planes meeting on a diameter of the sphere. Find its volume.

6.6 Moments: Moments of Inertia (in the Plane)

In mechanics, if a particle P of mass m is located at a distance s from a line L then we say that the *moment* of P about L is ms and that the *moment of inertia* of P about L is ms^2.

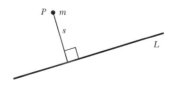

Fig. 6-22

To generalize to the case of continuous distribution of mass, integration is needed. The intuitive picture is that of a very large number of very small particles uniformly distributed over the region, or curve, considered. The subdivisions used are as usual (Fig. 6-23).

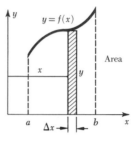

Fig. 6-23

We assume here unit density of mass distribution, hence the mass of each region is numerically equal to its area (or length).

Using $y\Delta x$, Δs for the masses of the strip and piece of arc, respectively, and x as the moment arm, we get moments $xy\Delta x$, $x\Delta s$ and moments of inertia $x^2 y\Delta x$, $x^2\Delta s$, respectively (Fig. 6-24). Hence,

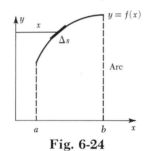

Fig. 6-24

for the entire region and arc we get

$$\text{(region) } M_y = \int_a^b x\,y\,dx, \quad \text{(arc) } M_y = \int_a^b x\,ds \quad \text{(moments about } y\text{-axis).}$$

$$\text{(region) } I_y = \int_a^b x^2\,y\,dx, \quad \text{(arc) } I_y = \int_a^b x^2\,ds \quad \text{(moments of inertia).}$$

In the cases of the arc, ds is replaced by

$$D_x s\,dx = \sqrt{1 + (D_x y)^2}\,dx$$

before proceeding with the evaluation of the integral. (Section 3.7.)

A fuller justification can be given for the use of the above integrals in evaluating moments and moments of inertia. We will outline such a justification in the case of M_y for a region (In Fig. 6-25, assume unit area density.)

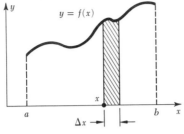

Fig. 6-25

Consider a vertical strip of the region (not just an approximating rectangle). Its area, and hence its mass, will be greater than or equal to Δx times the least value of $f(x)$ for x within the strip and less than or equal to Δx times the greatest value of $f(x)$ for x within it. Hence, using a continuity argument, it will be exactly equal to $f(x_1)\Delta x$ for some x_1 within the strip.

Now, if all the particles of matter were to be moved over to the left edge of the strip, with abscissa x, their combined moment would be decreased, becoming $xf(x_1)\Delta x$. Similarly their combined moment is less than $(x+\Delta x)f(x_1)\Delta x$. Hence the moment is exactly $x_2 f(x_1)\Delta x$ for some x_2 between x and $x+\Delta x$, and the total moment for the whole region is $\sum_{a}^{b} x_2 f(x_1)\Delta x$.

This is equal to $\lim_{\delta \to 0} \sum_{a}^{b} x_2 f(x_1)\Delta x$, since the limit of a constant is that constant itself.

It can be shown, however, that such a limit is the same as $\lim_{\delta \to 0} \sum_{a}^{b} \bar{x}f(\bar{x})\Delta x$, where $\bar{x}$ is any value between x and $x+\Delta x$, and this is the required definite integral.

In practice we will continue to use less precise arguments, such as appear with Figs. 6-23 and 6-24.

Examples

(i) For a rectangle with sides a, b as shown,

$$M_y = \int_0^a x\, b\, dx = \frac{a^2}{2} \cdot b\,,$$

$$I_y = \int_0^a x^2\, b\, dx = \frac{a^3}{3} \cdot b.$$

We note that M_y is the same as if the mass were concentrated at the center of the rectangle. For I_y this is not so.

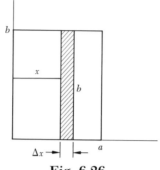

Fig. 6-26

We can apply the results of this example to find M_x and I_x in the more general case of the area under the curve $y = f(x)$.

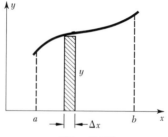

Fig. 6-27

To get the contribution of the element of area to M_x we note that the x-axis here plays the role of the y-axis in our example as the line with respect to which the moment is wanted. Thus y plays the role of a, and Δx plays the role of b.

$$M_y = \frac{a^2}{2} b$$

in the example thus yields

$$M_x = \frac{y^2}{2} \Delta x$$

for the element of area.
Taking the limit of the sum of such contributions gives

$$M_x = \int_a^b \frac{y^2}{2} \, dx$$

for the whole area.

Similarly

$$I_y = \frac{a^3}{3} b$$

Yields

$$I_x = \frac{y^3}{3} \Delta x$$

for the element of area and hence

$$I_x = \int_a^b \frac{y^3}{3} \, dx$$

for the whole area.

(ii) In the case of the parabolic arc $2y = x^2$ from $x = 0$ to 1 (Fig. 6-28),

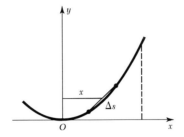

Fig. 6-28

$$M_y = \int_0^1 x \, ds$$

$$= \int_0^1 x \sqrt{1 + x^2} \, dx \text{ (since } D_x y = x)$$

$$= 1/2 \int_0^1 \sqrt{1 + x^2} \, d \, (1 + x^2)$$

$$= 1/3 \, (2\sqrt{2} - 1) \, .$$

For a quadrant of a circle

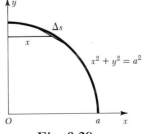

Fig. 6-29

$$I_y = \int_0^a x^2 \, ds$$

(Just as $D_x s = \sqrt{1 + (D_x y)^2}$, so is $D_y s = \sqrt{1 + (D_y x)^2}$)

$$= \int_0^a x^2 \sqrt{1 + (D_y x)^2} \, dy$$

$$= \int_0^a x^2 \sqrt{1 + \left(\frac{y}{x}\right)^2} \, dy$$

$$= \int_0^a x \sqrt{x^2 + y^2} \, dy$$

$$= \int_0^a x \, a \, dy$$

$$= \pi \frac{a^3}{4}.$$

$\left(\int_0^a x \, dy$ is obviously the area of the quadrant$\right)$.

Exercises

(Assume unit mass densities throughout: area or curvilinear, as the case may be.)

1. Find, for the rectangular region bounded by the axes and $x = 2$, $y = 1$, its moment and its moment of inertia about the line $x = 4$.

2. Find the moment about the x-axis of the parabolic arc $x = 4y^2$ from $y = 0$ to $y = 2$.

3. Find the moment of inertia of a thin rod (a) about one end; (b) about its center (i.e., about a line perpendicular to the rod through the point concerned).

4. Find the moment and the moment of inertia of a triangular region about one of its sides. What are the only dimensions affecting the answer?

5. Find the moment of inertia of the circumference of a circle with respect to a diameter.

6. Find the moment of inertia of a circular region about a line through its center and perpendicular to its plane.

7. Prove the *perpendicular-axis theorem*: the moment of inertia of a region or curve in a plane about a line perpendicular to the plane is equal to the sum of its moments of inertia about two mutually perpendicular lines in the plane and intersecting the given line. (*Hint*: consider the result for a single particle.)

Problems

8. Find the moment and the moment of inertia of a circular region with respect to a tangent line.

9. Find the moment of inertia of a circular region about a diameter, using the results of Exercises 6 and 7.

10. Find the moment of inertia of a cylinder about its axis.

11. A triangle has base b and height h. Find its moment of inertia about a line parallel to the base and through the opposite vertex.

12. Find the moment of inertia of a rectangle about a line through a vertex and perpendicular to the plane of the rectangle.

13. Find the moment of inertia of a sphere about a diameter. (Use the result of Exercise 6.)

6.7 Mass-Centers: The Theorems of Pappus

It can be shown (see Chapter 9) that, given a uniform plane distribution of matter, there exists a point C such that, given *any* line l in the plane, the moment of the total distribution about l is the same as if the mass were concentrated at C (Fig. 6-30). That is, $M = $ (total mass) $\cdot S$. The same applies to a uniform distribution of matter over a plane curve.

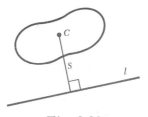

Fig. 6-30

In the case of a distribution of unit density along an arc, or over an area, we have (Figs. 6-31 and 6-32).

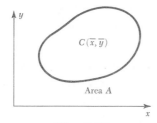

Fig. 6-31

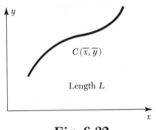

Fig. 6-32

Area	*Arc*
$A\bar{x}=M_y.$	$L\bar{x}=M_y.$
Hence $\bar{x}=\dfrac{M_y}{A}.$	Hence $\bar{x}=\dfrac{M_y}{L}.$
Similarly $\bar{y}=\dfrac{M_x}{A}.$	Similarly $\bar{y}=\dfrac{M_x}{L}.$

M_x, M_y, A, L, can be found as in previous sections (6.3, 6.4, 6.6).

The theorems of Pappus (c. 300 A.D.). A region R of area A is rotated about a straight line l which does not intersect it (Fig. 6-33).

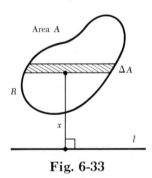

Fig. 6-33

To find the resulting volume swept out, we divide the region R into strips parallel to l. Let a typical strip have area ΔA, and be a distance x from l. Then, since each such strip travels a distance $2\pi x$, sweeping out a volume $2\pi x\,\Delta A$ (approximately), we have total volume $V=\int_R 2\pi x\,dA$ ($\int_R$ indicating integration over R.) Since $M_l=\int_R x\,dA=A\bar{x}$, where $\bar{x}$ is distance of mass-center from l, we have $V=A\cdot 2\pi\bar{x}=$ area $\times$ distance travelled by mass center.

Similarly, with a curve C (Fig. 6-34), area A swept out $=\int_C 2\pi\,x\,ds$ $=2\pi\int_C x\,ds=2\pi\,M_l=L\cdot 2\pi\,\bar{x}$. $A=$ length $\times$ distance travelled by mass-center.

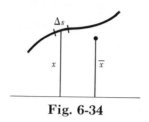

Fig. 6-34

Examples

(i) A circle of radius a is rotated about a line a distance b from its center where $b > a$ (Fig. 6-35). By symmetry the mass-center of the

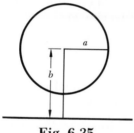

Fig. 6-35

circle is at its center. Hence volume swept out $=\pi a^2\cdot 2\pi b$ (Pappus) $=2\pi^2\,a^2 b$.

(ii) We can invert the process to find mass-centers. Consider a semi-circular arc of radius r (Fig. 6-36). The arc sweeps out a sphere of

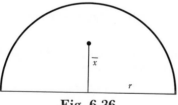

Fig. 6-36

surface area $4\pi r^2$ (its radius being r). Also, area $=2\pi\,\bar{x}\cdot\pi r$ (Pappus). Therefore $4r^2=2\bar{x}\cdot\pi r$, hence $\bar{x}=2r/\pi$.

Exercises

1. Find the centroid of a quadrant of the ellipse $x^2/a^2 + y^2/b^2 = 1$.
2. Find the centroid of the region bounded by $y = x^2$, $y = 0$, $x = 1$.
3. Find the centroid of the region bounded by $y^2 = x$, $y = x - 2$.
4. Find the centroid of the region bounded by $y = 4 - x^2$ and the positive x and y axes.

Problems

5. Find the surface area of the torus generated by revolving a circle about a line in its plane which does not intersect it.

6. Prove the *parallel-axis theorem:* the moment of inertia of a plane region about a line in its plane is equal to its moment of inertia about the parallel line through its centroid plus its area multiplied by the square of the distance K between the lines. (*Hint:* $(x + K)^2 = x^2 + 2xK + K^2$, and the term $2xK$ yields 0 on integrating.)

7. Use Problem 6 and the formula for the moment of inertia of a rectangle about a side to find the moment of inertia about any line parallel to a side.

8. Find the centroid of a semicircular region (a) by direct integration, (b) using a theorem of Pappus.

9. For the region bounded by $y = 1 - x^2$ and the x-axis, find (a) the volume generated by rotating it about the x-axis, (b) its centroid.

10. Use Problem 9, Section 6.6, to find the moment of inertia of a circular region about any line in its plane.

11. (a) Find the centroid of a sector of a circle by using polar coordinates. (*Hint:* use, as usual, a polar coordinate subdivision into triangles, then use the result of Problem 12 below in getting the contribution of each triangle.)
    (b) Find the volume got by rotating a sector of a circle about one of its bounding radii.

12. Prove that the centroid of a triangle is the point of intersection of the medians. (Do as an exercise in integration.)

13. Find the centroid of one loop of the curve $\rho = a \cos 2\theta$.

14. Find the centroid of half of the region inside the curve $\rho = a(1 - \sin\theta)$.

15. Find the centroid of the region bounded by $y^2 = 4x$ and $y = 2x - 4$.

16. Find the centroid of a semicircular arc by integration using polar coordinates. Check by using this result to find the surface area of a sphere.

6.8 Work

The physical concept of work in many instances is equivalent to a definite integral. We shall consider a number of examples by way of illustration.

(i) A 100-pound weight is hoisted 50 feet by a cable weighing 1 pound per foot, the cable being run over a pulley and pulled horizontally. Find the work done.

Solution: Think of dividing the cable into little pieces Δx at distances x from the top (Fig. 6-37). The work required to lift each

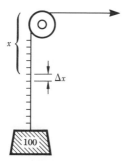

Fig. 6-37

piece is $x \cdot \Delta x$ (approximately) foot-pounds. Hence total work = work in lifting weight+work in lifting cable=$100 \times 50 + \int_0^{50} x \, dx$ foot-pounds.

(ii) A piston compresses the gas in a cylinder from a volume of 100 cubic feet to a volume of 10 cubic feet. The initial pressure is 10 pounds per square foot. Find the work done, assuming that (pressure · volume) is constant.

Solution: $pv = 10 \cdot 100 = 1000$. Let A be the area of cross-section of the cylinder (Fig. 6-38). The force due to pressure will be pA pounds.

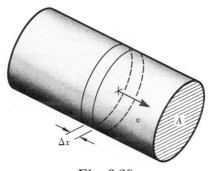

Fig. 6-38

The work in foot-pounds done during the compression Δx is $pA\Delta x$ (approximately). It is convenient to use the fact that $p(A\Delta x)$ is equal to $p\Delta v$, where Δv is the corresponding change in volume. Hence, total work done in foot-pounds $= \int_{v=100}^{10} -p\,dv$ (we use a minus sign because v decreases as x increases) $= \int_{10}^{100} \dfrac{1000}{v}\,dv$.

(iii)   A hemispherical tank of radius R is filled with a liquid of density w. Find the work required to pump out the liquid over the top.

Solution: We consider the liquid as divided into layers, the layer at depth x having thickness Δx (Fig. 6-39). Its radius is $\sqrt{(R^2-x^2)}$,

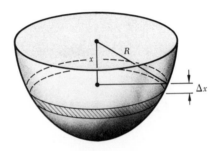

Fig. 6-39

hence its volume is $\pi(R^2-x^2)\Delta x$, and the work done in raising it to the top is (approximately) $xw\pi(R^2-x^2)\Delta x$. Hence, total work $= \int_0^R xw\pi(R^2-x^2)\,dx$. (*Note:* For convenience in this and subsequent examples we suppress the units involved. Thus "work done $= K$" means the same as "work done $= K$ units of work.")

Exercises

1. A thin obelisk weighs K pounds per foot of length and is h feet tall. Find the work done in raising it to an upright position.

2. A particle is moved along the x-axis from $x=1$ to $x=3$ against a resisting force equal to $10x$. Find the work done.

3. A spring is compressed 2 inches by a force of 100 pounds. How much work is required to compress it 1 inch?

4. Find the work done in compressing a cylinder of gas from 400 cubic feet at 10 pounds per square inch pressure to 100 cubic feet (assume pv is constant).

Problems

5. A pyramid has a square base of sides a and a height h. It is made of material weighing K pounds per unit volume. Find the work done in lifting the material during construction.

6. A conical tank of height h and radius r at the top is filled with a liquid of density w. Find the work done in pumping the liquid out over the top.

7. A force of K pounds will stretch a spring s inches. How much work is required to stretch it p inches?

8. A sphere of negligible weight has radius a. Find the work required to submerge it in a liquid of density w, assuming the container to be very large.

9. 120 inch-pounds of work are required to stretch a spring 4 inches. How much work is required to stretch it 2 inches?

10. A load of weight m is to be lifted from the bottom of a shaft h feet deep. The cable weighs w pounds per foot. Find the work done.

6.9 Pressure

The pressure (force per unit area) in a liquid depends on the depth below the surface, being wx, where x is the depth and w the density of the liquid. To find the total force due to pressure on a submerged area, we need integration. The following examples indicate the method used.

(i) Consider a rectangle of sides a and b submerged as shown in a liquid of density w (Fig. 6-40). We think of dividing the rectangle

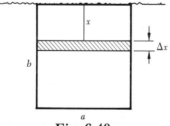

Fig. 6-40

into horizontal strips. The force due to pressure on one side of a typical strip, as indicated, is (pressure · its area) $= wx \cdot a\Delta x$ (approximately); therefore, total force $= \int_0^b wxa\,dx = wa\frac{b^2}{2}$. We note that this is the total area, ab, multiplied by the pressure at the centroid, $w(b/2)$.

(ii) A trough in the form of a half-cylinder of radius r is filled with liquid of density w (Fig. 6-41). What is the total force on one end?

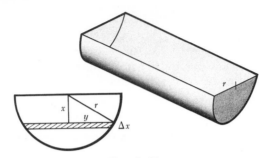

Fig. 6-41

We think of dividing the end area into horizontal strips. A typical strip has width Δx and length $2y = 2\sqrt{(r^2 - x^2)}$. The force on such a strip is $wx \cdot 2\sqrt{(r^2 - x^2)} \, \Delta x$ (approximately), hence total force $= \int_0^r w \, x \, 2\sqrt{(r^2 - x^2)} \, dx$.

(iii)   It can be shown quite generally that the *total force* is equal to *total area · pressure at centroid*. Consider a vertical submerged plane region A and a typical horizontal strip of area ΔA (Fig. 6-42).

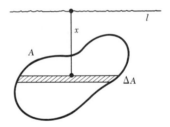

Fig. 6-42

The total force due to pressure is $\int_A wx \, dA$, where $\int_A$ denotes integration carried out over the entire region A.

$$\int_A wx \, dA = w_A \int x \, dA$$
$$= w \cdot M_l \quad \text{(where } l \text{ is the line of the surface)}$$
$$= w \cdot \bar{x} A \quad (\bar{x} \text{ being the distance of the centroid from } l)$$
$$= \text{pressure at centroid} \cdot A.$$

Exercises

1. A vertical dam has the form of a trapezoid 300 feet long at the surface of the water, 200 feet long at the bottom, and 60 feet high. Supposing

the water to weigh 62.5 pounds per cubic foot, what force due to pressure must the dam withstand?

2. A cylindrical tank of radius r is full of liquid of density w and is lying on its side. Find the total force due to pressure on one end.

Problems

3. Find the total pressure on a completely submerged sphere.

4. A rectangular plate of sides a and b is submerged vertically in a liquid of density w, its upper edge of length a being a depth h below the surface. Find, by integration, the total force due to pressure on one side, and check your answer by using the pressure at the centroid.

5. The ends of a trough are equilateral triangles of sides a, and the trough is K units long. If it is filled with liquid of density w, find the total force on its sloping sides.

6. A rectangular gate of dimensions a, b in the face of a dam has the side of length a at the water line. Find the total moment about the water line of the force due to pressure on the gate, and hence find the center of pressure. (The moment of a force about a line is the magnitude of the force multiplied by the distance between the given line and the line of action of the force. The center of pressure is the point at which a force equal to the total force must act in order to produce the total moment.)

7. Repeat Problem 6, assuming that the upper edge of length a is submerged a distance h. Does the center of pressure have the same position in the rectangle as it had previously?

6.10 Mean Values

The notion of *mean value* or *average* is a relative concept. That is, we always average *with respect to* something. For example, if one village has two inhabitants, with incomes of $1000 and $2000, and another village has only one inhabitant, with an income of $3000, then

$$\text{average income } per \ person = \frac{\$1000 + \$2000 + \$3000}{3} = \$2000,$$

$$\text{but average income } per \ village = \frac{\$3000 + \$3000}{2} = \$3000.$$

By use of the notion of a definite integral, one can extend the notion of a mean value to that of an infinite collection. For example, given a function, $f(x)$, and a range (a,b) for x (Fig. 6-43), we define

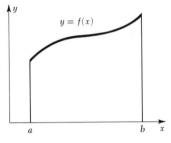

Fig. 6-43

the mean value of $f(x)$ over (a,b) *with respect to* x to be

$$\frac{\int_a^b f(x)\, dx}{b-a}.$$

This can be interpreted as (area under curve)/(base). In still other words: the mean value is the constant height which would give the same area.

This definition can be seen to arise out of the usual notion of the average of a finite number of values as follows: Divide the interval into equal pieces of length Δx (Fig. 6-44). Let the heights of the curve at the division points be $y_1, y_2 \ldots, y_n$. (The equal spacing amounts to equal "weighting" of the different portions of the curve with respect to x.) The average of these n heights is

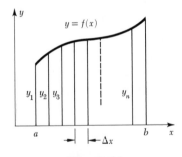

Fig. 6-44

$$\frac{y_1+y_2+\cdots+y_n}{n}=\frac{y_1\Delta x+y_2\Delta x+\cdots+y_n\Delta x}{n\Delta x}$$

$$=\sum_a^b \frac{y_i\Delta x}{(b-a)}=\sum_a^b \frac{f(x_i)\Delta x}{(b-a)}.$$

The limit as $n \to \infty$ is

$$\frac{\int_a^b f(x)\, dx}{b - a}.$$

Example: A point moves according to the law $x = t^2$, $y = t^4 + 2$, t ranging from 0 to 2.

$$(\text{Average value of } y \text{ with respect to } x) = \frac{\int_0^4 (x^2 + 2)\, dx}{4} = 7\frac{1}{3},$$

$$(\text{Average value of } y \text{ with respect to } t) = \frac{\int_0^2 (t^4 + 2)\, dt}{2} = 5\frac{1}{5}.$$

Exercises

1. Find the average value of $\sin^2 x$ with respect to x as x varies from 0 to 2π.

2. A body falls from rest under a constant acceleration g. Find its average velocity during the first T seconds (a) with respect to time, and (b) with respect to distance.

3. Given a finite number of particles of unit mass lying in a plane, show that their average distance from any line in the plane is equal to the distance of their mass-center from that line. (By "distance" is meant *directed* distance.)

4. A particle of mass m oscillates on the x-axis according to the law $x = r \cos wt$. Show that the average (with respect to time) kinetic energy is one-half the maximum kinetic energy.

5. Find the average, with respect to x, of the slope of the curve $y = f(x)$ between $x = a$ and $x = b$. Interpret your answer.

6. Find the average, with respect to θ, of the distance of the curve $\rho = e^\theta$ (polar coordinates) from the origin as θ varies from 0 to K.

7. Find the average of $a\,(1 + \cos \theta)$ with respect to θ as θ varies from 0 to 2π.

Problems

8. Find the average ordinate of the semicircle $y = \sqrt{1 - x^2}$, (a) with respect to arc length, and (b) with respect to x.

9. A body falls from rest under a constant acceleration g. It falls a distance

h. Prove that the average velocity (with respect to distance) is two-thirds the velocity at the end of the fall.

10. In Exercise 4, show that the average kinetic energy with respect to *distance* is two-thirds the maximum kinetic energy.

11. A point moves on a line of length *a*, producing two segments of lengths *x*, *a* − *x*. Prove that the average with respect to *x* of the product of these lengths is 1/6 *a*².

12. Interpret the centroids of an arc and of an area in terms of averages.

13. Given *pv* = *c*, where *c* is a constant, find the average of *p* with respect to *v* as *v* changes from v_1 to v_2.

6.11 Improper Integrals

The notion of a limit enables us to extend the definition of a definite integral to cases where the function being integrated becomes infinite somewhere in the interval of integration, and to cases where the limits of integration may be infinite.

The fact that we have previously assumed the integrand to be finite is brought out by the following example:

$$\int_{-1}^{1} \frac{1}{x^2}\,dx = -\frac{1}{x}\Big|_{-1}^{1} = -2?$$

The result is clearly not correct, since $1/x^2$ is never negative, hence the integral could not be negative. What has happened is that we have proceeded according to our usual routine, forgetting an assumption that was taken for granted in establishing that routine and that no longer holds—namely, the assumption that the integrand is defined for all values of *x* in the interval of integration. The expression $\int_{-1}^{1} 1/x^2\,dx$ must be regarded as meaningless until we extend our previous definition of the definite integral to include such cases.

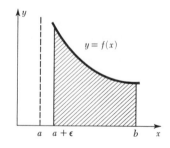

Assume *a* < *b*

Fig. 6-45

In Fig. 6-45, if $f(x) \to \infty$ as $x \to a$, then we define $\int_a^b f(x)\, dx$ to be $\lim_{\epsilon \to 0} \int_{a+\epsilon}^b f(x)\, dx$, if such a limit exists (ϵ being positive). If the discontinuity is at b, we use $\lim_{\epsilon \to 0} \int_a^{b-\epsilon} f(x)\, dx$, and if it is at c, where $a < c < b$, we take

$$\int_a^b f(x)\, dx = \int_a^c f(x)\, dx + \int_c^b f(x)\, dx,$$

where the last two integrals are of the above types. If such a limit does not exist, then we say that the integral doesn't exist, or is "divergent." The cases that interest us here are those where the integral exists.

Examples

(i)

$$\int_{-1}^1 \frac{1}{x^2}\, dx = \int_{-1}^0 \frac{1}{x^2}\, dx + \int_0^1 \frac{1}{x^2}\, dx$$

$$= \lim_{\epsilon \to 0} \int_{-1}^{-\epsilon} \frac{1}{x^2}\, dx + \lim_{\epsilon \to 0} \int_\epsilon^1 \frac{1}{x^2}\, dx$$

$$= \lim_{\epsilon \to 0} \left(\frac{+1}{\epsilon} - 1\right) + \lim_{\epsilon \to 0} \left(-1 + \frac{1}{\epsilon}\right).$$

Here both integrals diverge, so we say that the original integral diverges. In our initial effort, leading to the incorrect value -2, we managed somehow to neglect the terms $1/\epsilon$.

(ii)

$$\int_0^1 \frac{1}{x^{2/3}}\, dx = \lim_{\epsilon \to 0} \int_\epsilon^1 x^{-2/3}\, dx$$

$$= \lim_{\epsilon \to 0} 3x^{1/3} \Big|_\epsilon^1$$

$$= \lim_{\epsilon \to 0} 3 - 3\epsilon^{1/3} = 3.$$

Thus the integral exists and has the value 3 (see Fig. 6-46).

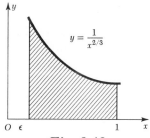

Fig. 6-46

A similar method can be used to define integrals over an infinite range. We define

$$\int_a^\infty f(x)\, dx \quad \text{to be} \quad \lim_{k\to\infty} \int_a^k f(x)\, dx,$$

and a similar definition is given when the lower limit is infinite.

(iii)

$$\int_1^\infty \frac{1}{x}\, dx \quad \text{means} \quad \lim_{k\to\infty} \int_1^k \frac{1}{x}\, dx = \lim_{k\to\infty} \ln x \Big|_1^k,$$

which diverges.

(iv) In Fig. 6-47, $y = 1/x^2$,

$$\int_1^\infty \frac{1}{x^2}\, dx = \lim_{k\to\infty} -\frac{1}{x}\Big|_1^k = 1.$$

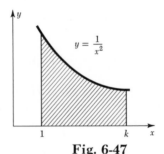

Fig. 6-47

The geometrical interpretation is that the area under the curve $y = 1/x^2$ from $x = 1$ to infinity is 1. Thus a region may be infinitely "long" yet have a finite area, as here defined.

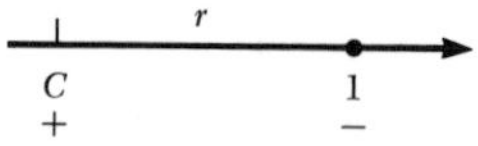

Fig. 6-48

(v) A unit negative charge is situated at a distance r from a positive charge C (Fig. 6-48). The work required to move the unit charge infinitely far away is (in suitable units), assuming the inverse square law of attraction,

$$\int_r^\infty \frac{C}{x^2}\, dx = \lim_{k\to\infty} \int_r^k \frac{C}{x^2}\, dx = \lim_{k\to\infty} -\frac{C}{x}\Big|_r^k = \frac{C}{r}.$$

This is what is known as the "potential" at the initial point.

Exercises

1. Evaluate $\int_0^\infty 1/(1+x)^2 \, dx$.

2. Find the area between $y = 1/(1+x^2)$ and the x-axis.

3. Evaluate $\int_{-\infty}^1 e^x \, dx$.

4. Evaluate $\int_1^\infty 1/x^4 \, dx$.

5. Evaluate $\int_0^a 1/\sqrt{a^2 - x^2} \, dx$.

6. Evaluate $\int_0^\infty e^{-4y} \, dy$.

Problems

7. Find the centroid of the region bounded by e^{-x} and the axes.

8. Find the area under $y = 1/x$ from $x = 0$ to $x = 1$. Find the volume obtained by rotating this region about the y-axis.

9. Find the area between $y = xe^{-(1/2)x^2}$ and $y = 0$.

10. Find the area bounded by $y = (x^2 - 1)/(x^2 + 1)$ and $y = 1$.

11. Evaluate $\int_0^4 1/(x^2 - 2x - 3) \, dx$.

12. Show how the value of $\int_0^\infty e^{-Kt} \, dt$ depends on K.

13. Produce an example where

$$\lim_{K \to 0} \left[\int_{-1}^{-K} f(x) \, dx + \int_K^1 f(x) \, dx \right] \neq \lim_{K \to 0} \int_{-1}^{-K} f(x) \, dx + \lim_{K \to 0} \int_K^1 f(x) \, dx.$$

14. Find the volume generated by rotating the region bounded by $y = e^{-x}$ and the axes about the x-axis.

15. Show how the convergence or divergence of $\int_a^b 1/(x-a)^K \, dx$ depends on the value of K.

Miscellaneous

16. The value of land is $10/(1+s)$ dollars per unit area at a distance s from a given point. Find the total value of a circular region of radius r with center at the given point.

17. A ship consumes fuel at the rate of $K/(w+x)$ miles per gallon, where K

and w are constants and x is the number of gallons of fuel on board. How far can it go on g gallons of fuel?

18. The velocity function of a point moving along the x-axis is $v(x)$. How long does it take to travel from $x=a$ to $x=b$? Explain fully your method.

19. The velocity function of a point is $v(t)$ at time t. How far does it travel between times $t=0$ and $t=1$? Explain fully your method.

20. The velocity function of a point moving along the x-axis is x^2, and $x=1$ when $t=1$. How far does it travel between times $t=1$ and $t=1 \cdot 5$?

7

Infinite Series

The fundamental operations of arithmetic are $+$, $-$, $\times$, $\div$. When a formula is expressed entirely in these terms, then we know how to compute its value. For example, if $f(x) = (x^3 + 5x)\, x^9$, then we can proceed by routine methods to find $f(5)$ in decimal form to as many significant figures as we like.

Can the same be said of other functions, for example $\sin x$, $\ln 1/x$, $\cos 4x$? Is it possible to find a formula of the above type for $\sin x$? For example, is

$$\sin x = \frac{2x^7 + 9x^2}{x^9 - 2}?$$

If we are willing to admit "infinitely many" applications of the operations $+$, $-$, $\times$, $\div$, then we *can* express all familiar functions in terms of them (possibly with some restrictions on the range of the variable, x). The result will be a unified approach to the elementary functions, which will shed new light on their relationships with one another and provide methods of computation of tables of values.

What is meant here by an "infinite" process is another application of the notion of a *limit*, namely the concept of an *infinite series*.

Before going on with a systematic account of this topic, let us assume for a moment that infinite series behave just like finite sums and see what results we get; later on we will justify the steps we have taken.

A familiar example of an infinite series is the formula

$$\frac{a}{1+x} = a - ax + ax^2 - \cdots, \text{ where } |x| < 1$$

(the sum of an infinite G. P.).

149

No matter what the value of x may be (between -1 and 1), the rational function on the left is equal to the infinite "polynomial" on the right. The right side, of course, represents a limiting process in which, as we take more and more terms, we get closer and closer, and arbitrarily close, to the limit value.

The latter clause means that no matter how small a number, $\epsilon > 0$, is chosen, we can always take enough terms so that, for that many terms *or more*, the sum is within ϵ of the limit. Thus, the sequence

$$a$$
$$a - ax$$
$$a - ax + ax^2$$
$$a - ax + ax^2 - ax^3$$
$$\cdots$$
$$\cdots$$
$$\cdots$$

approaches $a/(1+x)$ as limit.

Next we have two examples where, from the fact that the *derivative* of a function can be written as a series, we get (by anti-differentiating) the function itself expressed as a series.

(i)

$$D_x \ln (1+x) = \frac{1}{1+x}$$

$$= 1 - x + x^2 - x^3 + x^4 - \cdots.$$

Hence, anti-differentiating,

$$\ln (1+x) = x - \frac{x^2}{2} + \frac{x^3}{3} - \frac{x^4}{4} + \frac{x^5}{5} - \cdots + C \qquad \text{(some constant)}.$$

Since $\ln 1 = 0$, we get $C = 0$ on putting $x = 0$. As a special case, putting $x = 1$ we get $\ln 2 = 1 - 1/2 + 1/3 - 1/4 + 1/5 - \cdots$, a remarkable result connecting $\ln 2$ with the reciprocals of the integers.

(ii)

$$D_x \tan^{-1} x = \frac{1}{1+x^2}$$

$$= 1 - x^2 + x^4 - x^6 + \cdots.$$

Hence

$$\tan^{-1} x = x - \frac{x^3}{3} + \frac{x^5}{5} - \frac{x^7}{7} + \cdots + C.$$

Since $\tan^{-1} 0 = 0$, we get $C = 0$. Putting $x = 1$ gives the formula

$$\frac{\pi}{4} = 1 - \frac{1}{3} + \frac{1}{5} - \frac{1}{7} + \cdots.$$

Thus

$$\pi = 4\left(1 - \frac{1}{3} + \frac{1}{5} - \frac{1}{7} + \cdots\right),$$

another remarkable formula.

We can see the need for further investigation, however, for if in the above we put $x = 2$, we get

$$\tan^{-1} 2 = (?) \, 2 - \frac{8}{3} + \frac{32}{5} - \frac{128}{7} + \cdots.$$

The left side is a finite, fixed value, but the right side indicates a process that doesn't lead to any limit at all, the sums oscillating wider and wider as we keep adding more terms. Clearly our methods need a closer scrutiny.

Exercises

(All expansions are to be in powers of x unless otherwise stated.)

1. By the method used in the text on $\ln(1+x)$, derive series expansions of
   (a) $\ln(1-x)$, (b) $\sin^{-1} x$ [assume here that the binomial expansion of $(1-x^2)^{-(1/2)}$ is valid].

2. (a) Complete the discussion of $\ln(1+x)$ by giving the nth term in the expansion of $1/(1+x)$ and anti-differentiating it.
   (b) Do the same for $\tan^{-1} x$.

7.1 The Meaning of an Infinite Series (Constant Terms)

Given a sequence of numbers $a_1, a_2, a_3, \ldots, a_n, \ldots$ (for example, by being given a formula for the nth number) we consider the sequence of sums

$$\begin{aligned}
S_1 &= a_1, \\
S_2 &= a_1 + a_2, \\
S_3 &= a_1 + a_2 + a_3, \\
&\cdots \\
S_n &= a_1 + a_2 + a_3 + \cdots + a_n.
\end{aligned}$$

If S_n tends to a limit L as n tends to infinity, then we say that

$$L = a_1 + a_2 + a_3 + \cdots + a_n + \cdots$$

and call L the *sum* of the *infinite series* on the right. If S_n does not approach a limit, then we say that the series *diverges*.

Examples

(i)

$$1 + \frac{1}{2} + \left(\frac{1}{2}\right)^2 + \left(\frac{1}{2}\right)^3 + \cdots.$$

Here

$$S_n = \frac{1((1/2)^n - 1)}{(1/2) - 1} \quad \text{which} \rightarrow 2 \text{ as } n \rightarrow \infty.$$

The series hence *converges* and has *sum* 2.

(ii)

$$1 + 2 + 3 + \cdots.$$

S_n clearly $\rightarrow \infty$ as $n \rightarrow \infty$. The series *diverges*.

(iii)

$$1 - 1 + 1 - 1 + 1 - \cdots.$$

S_n is alternately $+1$ and 0, hence approaches no limit. The series *diverges*.

The problem of deciding whether or not a given series converges now arises. In general there is no routine procedure for testing for convergence. However, there are numerous tests that apply in most of the cases arising in practice, and to these we now turn.

Exercises

1. A series is not completely determined until, directly or indirectly, a formula is given for the nth term as a function of n. In the following cases, give a formula for the nth term that will specify the series completely. (The answer is not unique, although usually only one *simple* formula will satisfy the requirement).

(a) $2 + 4 + 6 + 8 + \cdots$,

(b) $1 - 3 + 5 - 7 + \cdots$,

(c) $1 + \frac{2}{3} + \frac{3}{5} + \frac{4}{7} + \cdots$,

(d) $1 - \frac{x}{2!} + \frac{x^2}{3!} - \frac{x^3}{4!} + \cdots$,

(e) $1 + \frac{1}{4} + \frac{1}{9} + \frac{1}{16} + \cdots$,

(f) $1 - \frac{x}{4!} + \frac{x^2}{7!} - \frac{x^3}{10!} + \cdots$.

2. Write down the first four terms and the $(n+1)$th term of the series whose nth term is

(a) $2n+1$,

(b) $(n-2)(-x)^n$,

(c) $\dfrac{(-1)^{n-1}x^{2n-1}}{(2n-1)!}$,

(d) $\dfrac{(-1)^{n+1}}{2n+1}$,

(e) $\dfrac{1}{3n-1}$,

(f) $\dfrac{(-1)^n}{n(n+1)}$.

7.2 A Necessary Condition for Convergence

THEOREM: If $a_1+a_2+\cdots+a_n+\cdots$ converges, then it is necessary that $a_n\to 0$ as $n\to\infty$.

For a proof we just note that $a_n=S_n-S_{n-1}$ and S_n and S_{n-1} both approach the limit L (S_{n-1} is just one step behind S_n), hence

$$\lim_{n\to\infty} a_n=\lim_{n\to\infty} S_n-\lim_{n\to\infty} S_{n-1}=0.$$

Note that $a_n\to 0$ does *not* guarantee convergence, however (that is, it is not a *sufficient* condition for convergence). For example, consider

$$1+\frac{1}{2}+\frac{1}{3}+\frac{1}{4}+\cdots+\frac{1}{n}+\cdots.$$

The first term is 1, the second 1/2, and the sums of the next 2 terms, the following 4, the following 8, etc., are each $>1/2$. Hence the adding process amounts to $1+(>1/2)+(>1/2)+(>1/2)+\cdots$, which clearly diverges, even though $(1/n)\to 0$ as $n\to\infty$.

7.3 The Integral Test (Positive Terms)

Consider a series $a_1+a_2+\cdots+a_n+\cdots$ of *positive* terms, where for a certain function f, $a_n=f(n)$ for every positive integer n, and where $f(x)$ decreases steadily as x increases over the range of real numbers. (For example, if $f(n)=1/n^2$, the series is $1+1/4+1/9+\cdots+1/n^2+\cdots$ and $f(x)=1/x^2$ decreases steadily.) The terms may be interpreted as the areas of the rectangles indicated in Fig. 7-1.

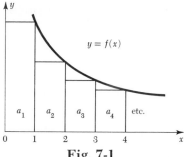

Fig. 7-1

I. If $\displaystyle\int_1^\infty f(x)\,dx$ converges, then the series converges.

Proof: Omitting the first term, a_1, clearly will not affect the convergence or divergence of the series. The successive sums of the areas of the remaining rectangles are clearly less than the total area under the curve from $x=1$ to infinity, which equals L (finite) by assumption.

Thus S_n increases but remains less than L. Hence it is intuitively evident that S_n approaches a limit and the series converges. (If S_n increases with n but is bounded above, then S_n approaches a limit; this is an important theorem that can be proved quite rigorously.)

II. If $\displaystyle\int_1^\infty f(x)\,dx$ diverges, then the series diverges.

Proof: Suppose the integral diverges. Let us turn all the rectangles over, as indicated in Fig. 7-2 (each rectangle in Fig. 7-1 being rotated about its right side). The total area of the rectangles always exceeds the area under the curve, which $\to\infty$. Hence the series diverges.

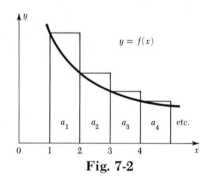

$$y = f(x)$$

Fig. 7-2

(The lower limit of the integral need not be taken as 1 in either case. We can ignore the first K terms of the sequence, for any K, without affecting the convergence of the sequence. We would do this, for example, if the conditions of the theorem held only for $n > K$; we would then take the lower limit to be $K+1$).

Examples

(i) $1 + 1/2 + 1/3 + \cdots + 1/n + \cdots.$ Here $f(n) = 1/n$.

$$\int_1^\infty \frac{1}{x}\,dx = \lim_{k\to\infty} \ln x\,\Big|_1^k ,$$

which is infinite and hence the series diverges.

(ii) $1 + 1/2^R + 1/3^R + \cdots + 1/n^R + \cdots$ $(R > 1)$. Here $f(n) = 1/n^R$.

$$\int_1^\infty \frac{1}{x^R}\,dx = \lim_{k \to \infty} \left.\frac{x^{-R+1}}{1-R}\right|_1^k = \lim_{k \to \infty} \frac{K^{1-R}}{1-R} - \frac{1}{1-R} = \frac{1}{R-1} \ ,$$

which is finite; hence the series converges.

7.4 Comparison Tests (Positive Terms)

Very often a series can be shown to converge (or diverge) by comparing its terms with those of a series which is known to converge (or diverge).

I. If $b_1 + b_2 + \cdots + b_n + \cdots$ (*positive* terms) converges and if $0 \le a_n \le b_n$ for all n, then $a_1 + a_2 + \cdots + a_n + \cdots$ converges.

Proof: Let the sum of the first series be B. Clearly $A_n = a_1 + a_2 + \cdots a_n \le B$, and increases with n. Hence A_n approaches a limit as $n \to \infty$. That is, the second series converges.

II. If $b_1 + b_2 + \cdots + b_n + \cdots$ (*positive* terms) diverges and $b_n \le a_n$ for all n, then $a_1 + a_2 + \cdots + a_n + \cdots$ diverges.

Proof: If $a_1 + a_2 + \cdots + a_n + \cdots$ converged, then $b_1 + b_2 + \cdots + b_n + \cdots$ would converge, by I, contrary to assumption.

Examples

(i) $1 + 1/2 + 1/3 + \cdots + 1/n + \cdots$ diverges. $1/\sqrt{n} \ge 1/n$ for all n. Hence $1 + 1/\sqrt{2} + 1/\sqrt{3} + \cdots + 1/\sqrt{n} + \cdots$ diverges.

(ii) $1 + 1/2 + 1/2^2 + \cdots + 1/2^n + \cdots$ converges. $1/[(n+1)\,2^n] \le 1/2^n$ for all n. Hence $1 + 1/(2 \cdot 2) + 1/(3 \cdot 2^2) + \cdots + 1/[(n+1)2^n] + \cdots$ converges.

7.5 The Ratio Test (Positive Terms)

Roughly speaking, a series converges if its terms tend to 0 "fast enough." The value of a_{n+1}/a_n is an indication of how rapidly the terms are decreasing. Actually, what matters is what eventually happens, as n gets larger and larger, so we are led to consider the value of

$$\lim_{n \to \infty} \frac{a_{n+1}}{a_n}.$$

We consider here only series of positive terms.

THEOREM: (The Ratio Test):
Let $\lim_{n \to \infty} a_{n+1}/a_n = L$. The series $a_1 + a_2 + \cdots + a_n + \cdots$

   I. *converges if $L < 1$.*
   II. *diverges if $L > 1$.*
(If $L = 1$, other tests are required.)

   Proof:

   I. Suppose $L < 1$. Then a_{n+1}/a_n eventually gets, and remains, arbitrarily close to L, hence $a_{n+1}/a_n < $ (some r) < 1 for n sufficiently large. From this value of n on, we have

$$a_{n+1} < r\, a_n,$$
$$a_{n+2} < r\, a_{n+1} < r^2\, a_n,$$
$$a_{n+3} < r\, a_{n+2} < r^3\, a_n, \text{ etc.}$$

Thus the terms of $a_{n+1} + a_{n+2} + a_{n+3} + \cdots$ are less in value than those of $ra_n + r^2 a_n + r^3 a_n + \cdots$, which is a convergent G.P. ($r < 1$). Hence $a_{n+1} + a_{n+2} + a_{n+3} + \cdots$ converges, and so does the entire original series.
   II. Suppose $L > 1$. Then eventually $a_{n+1}/a_n > 1$, so that the terms increase and the series obviously diverges.

Examples

   (i) $1 + 1/2 + 1/3 + \cdots + 1/n + \cdots$ diverges, $1 + 1/2^2 + 1/3^2 + \cdots + 1/n^2 + \cdots$ converges, and in each case $L = 1$. (*Exercise:* prove this.) Thus we see that from $L = 1$ neither convergence nor divergence need necessarily follow.
   (ii) $1 + 1/2! + 1/3! + \cdots + 1/n! + 1/(n+1)! + \cdots$.   Here

$$a_{n+1}/a_n = n!/(n+1)! = 1/(n+1),$$

which approaches 0 as $n \to \infty$. Thus $L = 0 < 1$, and the series converges. ($L = 0$ indicates very rapid convergence, since it means that eventually each term is "negligible" compared to its predecessor.)
   (iii) $k/1! + k^2/2! + k^3/3! + \cdots + k^n/n! + k^{n+1}/(n+1)! + \cdots$ (for arbitrary K). Here $a_{n+1}/a_n = k^{n+1}/(n+1)! \cdot n!/k^n = k/(n+1)$, which approaches 0 (as $n \to \infty$). Here the series converges. This example shows that the factorials increase so rapidly that even the sequence of powers in the numerators cannot prevent convergence.

7.6 Series with Positive and Negative Terms

   Generally speaking, series with infinitely many positive and negative terms are more likely to converge than are wholly positive or negative series. On the other hand, their behavior can be somewhat more complicated, since the successive sums may oscillate in value.

It is natural to try first to draw some conclusions from the behavior of the corresponding series of absolute values.

THEOREM: If $|a_1|+|a_2|+\cdots+|a_n|+\cdots$ *converges, then* $a_1+a_2+\cdots+a_n+\cdots$ *converges.*

Proof: We make use of the "in between" series of corresponding averages, $\dfrac{|a_n|+a_n}{2}$.

Consider $S_n = a_1 + \cdots + a_n$,
$$A_n = |a_1| + \cdots + |a_n|,$$
$$B_n = \frac{|a_1|+a_1}{2} + \cdots + \frac{|a_n|+a_n}{2}.$$

The terms of B_n are all positive or zero and are less than or equal to the terms of A_n. A_n converges (by assumption), hence B_n converges (by comparison). Clearly,

$$B_n = \frac{S_n}{2} + \frac{A_n}{2};$$

hence

$$S_n = 2\left(B_n - \frac{A_n}{2}\right),$$

which tends to $2\,(B - A/2)$, where B, A are the limits of B_n and A_n. Thus the series $a_1 + a_2 + \cdots a_n + \cdots$ converges.

The converse is not true. Thus, the fact that a series converges does not guarantee convergence of the corresponding series of absolute values. (Examples will be seen in subsequent sections.)

7.7 Alternating Series

If a series contains infinitely many positive and negative terms, then, by gathering together adjoining terms of the same sign, the series can be written as

$$a_1 - a_2 + a_3 - a_4 + a_5 - \cdots,$$

where the a's are all positive. (We allow a_1 to be 0.) Such a series is said to be "alternating." The following theorem enables us to prove at a glance the convergence of most of the common alternating series:

THEOREM: If $a_n > a_{n+1}$ *for all* n, *and* $a_n \to 0$ *as* n *increases, then the series* $a_1 - a_2 + a_3 - a_4 + \cdots$ *converges* (a's *all positive*).

Proof: Each term added (or subtracted) is less than the term previously subtracted (or added), hence the value of S_n oscillates, with a range of oscillation tending to zero (since $a_n \to 0$), and therefore approaches a limit. Note that, because of the nature of this oscillation, the absolute error committed in stopping the series at a given point is at most the absolute value of the term last used.

More formally, for n even,

$$S_n = (a_1 - a_2) + (a_3 - a_4) + \cdots + (a_{n-1} - a_n),$$

and also

$$S_n = a_1 - (a_2 - a_3) - (a_4 - a_5) - (a_{n-2} - a_{n-1}) - a_n.$$

The first expression shows S_n to be increasing, and the second shows it to be always less than a_1. Hence S_n approaches a limit, say S (n even). For the odd sums, we consider S_{n+1} (n even).

$$S_{n+1} = S_n + a_{n+1}.$$

Since $a_{n+1} \to 0$, S_{n+1} clearly $\to S$. Hence S_n (n even *or* odd) $\to S$.

Example: $1 - 1/2 + 1/3 - 1/4 + 1/5 - \cdots$ converges (to ln 2, in fact; note that $1 + 1/2 + 1/3 + 1/4 + \cdots$ does *not* converge).

Exercises

1. Test the following series for convergence:

(a) $1 - \dfrac{1}{3} + \dfrac{1}{5} - \cdots + \dfrac{(-1)^{n-1}}{2n-1} + \cdots,$

(b) $1 + \dfrac{1}{3} + \dfrac{1}{5} + \cdots + \dfrac{1}{2n-1} + \cdots,$

(c) $1 + \dfrac{4}{2 \cdot 5} + \dfrac{4^2}{3 \cdot 5^2} + \cdots + \dfrac{4^{n-1}}{n \cdot 5^{n-1}} + \cdots,$

(d) $\dfrac{1}{2} + \dfrac{3}{2^3} + \dfrac{5}{2^5} + \cdots + \dfrac{2n-1}{2^{2n-1}} + \cdots,$

(e) $1 - \dfrac{1}{\sqrt{2}} + \dfrac{1}{\sqrt{3}} - \cdots + \dfrac{(-1)^{n-1}}{\sqrt{n}} + \cdots,$

(f) $1 + \dfrac{1}{\sqrt{2}} + \dfrac{1}{\sqrt{3}} + \cdots + \dfrac{1}{\sqrt{n}} + \cdots.$

In the following cases, find the obvious nth term and test for convergence:

(g) $1 - \dfrac{1}{\sqrt{3}} + \dfrac{1}{\sqrt{5}} - \dfrac{1}{\sqrt{7}} + \cdots,$

(h) $1 + \dfrac{1}{\sqrt{3}} + \dfrac{1}{\sqrt{5}} + \dfrac{1}{\sqrt{7}} + \cdots,$

(i) $\dfrac{1}{3} + \dfrac{2!}{3^2} + \dfrac{3!}{3^3} + \dfrac{4!}{3^4} + \cdots,$

(j) $\dfrac{3}{1 \cdot 2} - \dfrac{4}{2 \cdot 3} + \dfrac{5}{3 \cdot 4} - \dfrac{6}{4 \cdot 5} + \cdots,$

(k) $\dfrac{3}{1 \cdot 2} + \dfrac{4}{2 \cdot 3} + \dfrac{5}{3 \cdot 4} + \dfrac{6}{4 \cdot 5} + \cdots.$

7.8 Rearrangement of Terms

In this section we will show that rearranging the terms of an infinite series may change its sum. This is a striking contrast with the sum of a finite number of expressions. In fact, it will be shown that by suitable rearrangement of the terms of $1 - 1/2 + 1/3 - 1/4 + \ldots$, the sum can be made anything at all.

First we note that the series (1) $1 + 1/3 + 1/5 + 1/7 + \cdots$ and, (2) $1/2 + 1/4 + 1/6 + 1/8 + \cdots$ both diverge (easily seen).

Suppose we want our sum to be K. We take just enough terms of (1) to get a sum $> K$. Then we subtract terms of (2) until the sum is just $< K$. Then we add remaining terms of (1) until the sum is just $> K$, etc. (The divergence of (1) and (2) guarantees that these things can actually be done). The resulting sums oscillate about the value K, with an amplitude which approaches zero. Hence their limit is K itself.

7.9 Series of Functions

If $u_1(x)$, $u_2(x)$, $u_3(x)$, $\cdots$, $u_n(x)$, $\cdots$ is a sequence of functions, then $u_1(x) + u_2(x) + \cdots + u_n(x) + \cdots$ for each given x gives a series that may converge or diverge. Thus, over the set of values of x for which it converges, it gives a function of x, the value of the function being the sum of the corresponding series.

We shall investigate here the question of whether the members of our familiar family of functions are expressible as series of the form (power series) $a_0 + a_1 x + a_2 x^2 + a_3 x^3 + \cdots + a_n x^n + \cdots$ or possibly, $a_0 + a_1(x - k) + a_2(x - k)^2 + a_3(x - k)^3 + \cdots$, where the a's and k are constants (depending on the function). The answer will be that they are so expressible. Moreover, in most cases the coefficients follow a very simple pattern.

7.10 The Interval of Convergence of a Power Series

THEOREM: For each power series there is a number r such that the series converges for x inside $(-r, r)$ and diverges for x outside $(-r, r)$. (The endpoints, $\pm r$, are in doubt.)

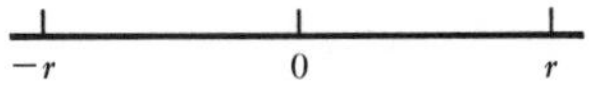

Fig. 7-3

Proof: We show that if the series converges for one value of x, then it converges for all values nearer 0 (positive or negative). This clearly implies that the range of convergence is as indicated, allowing r to be 0 or infinite if necessary.

Suppose that $a_0 + a_1 k + a_2 k^2 + \cdots + a_n k^n + \cdots$ converges, and consider x, where $|x| < |k|$. Since the series in k converges, $|a_n k^n| \to 0$ as n increases. Hence there is some finite value M which $|a_n k^n|$ never exceeds; that is, $|a_n k^n| < M$ always. Now $|x| < |k|$, hence $|x| \leq q|k|$ where $0 < q < 1$. This enables us to say that

$$|a_n x^n| \leq |a_n q^n k^n| = q^n |a_n k^n| < q^n M.$$

Thus the terms of $|a_0| + |a_1 x| + |a_2 x^2| + \cdots$ are less than those of $M + qM + q^2 M + \cdots$ (respectively), which is a convergent G. P. since $q < 1$. Hence $|a_0| + |a_1 x| + |a_2 x^2| + \cdots$ converges, and hence $a_0 + a_1 x + a_2 x^2 + \cdots$ converges. We have actually proved that the given series in x is *absolutely convergent*—that is, that the series of absolute values converges. *Thus, the interval of absolute convergence is the same as the interval of convergence, except possibly for the endpoints.*

The interval of convergence can frequently be found by first of all getting L of the ratio test as a function of x and then setting $L < 1$. For example, consider the series

$$1 - x + \frac{x^2}{2} - \frac{x^3}{3} + \cdots + \frac{(-x)^{n-1}}{n-1} + \cdots$$

(the formula for the nth term holding for all terms but the first).

$$\left| \frac{a_{n+1}}{a_n} \right| = \left| \frac{(-x)^n}{n} \cdot \frac{(n-1)}{(-x)^{n-1}} \right|$$

$$= \left| -x \cdot \left(1 - \frac{1}{n} \right) \right|.$$

This approaches $L = |x|$ as $n \to \infty$. Hence the required interval of convergence is $|x| < 1$, that is, $-1 < x < 1$, plus perhaps one or both of the endpoints. By putting $x = 1, -1$ we can easily show that the complete interval is $-1 < x \leq 1$.

(*Question:* why did we use absolute values?)

Exercises

1. Find the intervals of convergence of the following series:
   (a) $1 + x + x^2 + \cdots + x^{n-1} + \cdots$,
   (b) $1 + x + \dfrac{x^2}{2} + \dfrac{x^3}{3} + \cdots + \dfrac{x^{n-1}}{n-1} + \cdots$,
   (c) $1 + 2x + 4x^2 + 8x^3 + \cdots + 2^{n-1} x^{n-1} + \cdots$,
   (d) $x - \dfrac{x^2}{2} + \dfrac{x^3}{3} - \cdots + (-1)^{n-1} \dfrac{x^n}{n} + \cdots$,
   (e) $x + \dfrac{x^2}{\sqrt{2}} + \dfrac{x^3}{\sqrt{3}} + \cdots + \dfrac{x^n}{\sqrt{n}} + \cdots$.

7.11 The Expansion of $\ln (1+x)$ (for $-1 < x \leqslant 1$)

We begin by observing that

$$\ln (1+x) = \int_0^x \frac{dt}{1+t}$$

and that

$$\frac{1}{1+t} = 1 - t + t^2 - \cdots + (-1)^{n-1} t^{n-1} + \cdots$$

(a G.P. with ratio $-t$). The idea is to replace the integrand, $1/(1+t)$, by its series expansion and integrate term by term. Care must be taken, however, in such procedures. Summing the remaining terms of the above series, we have

$$\frac{1}{1+t} = 1 - t + t^2 - \cdots + (-1)^{n-1} t^{n-1} + \frac{(-1)^n t^n}{1+t}.$$

This gives a finite expression to work with. We are now justified in saying

$$\int_0^x \frac{dt}{1+t} = x - \frac{x^2}{2} + \frac{x^3}{3} - \cdots + (-1)^{n-1} \frac{x^n}{n} + (-1)^n \int_0^x \frac{t^n dt}{1+t}.$$

Next we show that the last integral approaches 0 as n increases. The cases $0 \leqslant x \leqslant 1$, $-1 < x < 0$ will be treated separately. If $0 \leqslant x \leqslant 1$, then $t^n/(1+t) < t^n$ as t ranges from 0 to x. Hence

$$\int_0^x \frac{t^n}{1+t} dt < \int_0^x t^n \, dt = \frac{x^{n+1}}{n+1},$$

which approaches 0 as n increases (since $|x| \leqslant 1$). If $-1 < x < 0$, then $|t^n/(1+t)| \leqslant |t^n/(1+x)|$ as t ranges from 0 to x (x is fixed); hence

$$\left| \int_0^x \frac{t^n}{1+t} dt \right| \leqslant \frac{1}{1+x} \int_0^{|x|} t^n \, dt = \frac{|x|^{n+1}}{(1+x)(n+1)},$$

which approaches 0 as n increases. Hence

$$\ln (1+x) = x - \frac{x^2}{2} + \frac{x^3}{3} - \cdots + (-1)^{n-1} \frac{x^n}{n} + R_n,$$

where R_n approaches 0 as n increases—that is,

$$\ln (1+x) = x - \frac{x^2}{2} + \frac{x^3}{3} - \cdots + (-1)^{n-1} \frac{x^n}{n} + (-1)^n \frac{x^{n+1}}{n+1} + \cdots.$$

If $x = -1$, the series clearly diverges.

7.12 Taylor's Series

We shall be content here to *assume* that our functions have infinite series expansions, and that it is permissible to differentiate infinite series term by term. Assuming this, it is possible to derive a general formula for the expansion of an arbitrary function. (This formula can be rigorously proved if certain restrictions are imposed on the function.) The procedure is simple. Assume that

$$f(x) = a_0 + a_1 x + a_2 x^2 + a_3 x^3 + a_4 x^4 + \cdots.$$

Setting $x = 0$ gives

$$\underline{f(0) = a_0}.$$

Differentiating gives

$$f'(x) = a_1 + 2a_2 x + 3a_3 x^2 + 4a_4 x^3 + \cdots.$$

Setting $x = 0$ gives

$$\underline{f'(0) = a_1}.$$

Differentiating gives

$$f''(x) = 2a_2 + 3 \cdot 2\, a_3 x + 4 \cdot 3\, a_4 x^2 + \cdots.$$

Setting $x = 0$ gives

$$\underline{f''(0) = 2a_2}.$$

Differentiating gives

$$f'''(x) = 3 \cdot 2\, a_3 + 4 \cdot 3 \cdot 2 a_4 x + \cdots.$$

Setting $x = 0$ gives

$$\underline{f'''(0) = 3 \cdot 2a_3}.$$

$$\vdots \text{ etc.}$$

Generally, we get

$$\underline{f^{(n)}(0) = n!\, a_n}$$

or

$$a_n = \frac{f^{(n)}(0)}{n!}.$$

Hence

$$f(x) = f(0) + \frac{f'(0)x}{1} + \frac{f''(0)x^2}{2!} + \frac{f'''(0)x^3}{3!} + \cdots + \frac{f^{(n)}(0)}{n!} x^n + \cdots.$$

This is called Taylor's Series (sometimes MacLaurin's).

One remarkable feature of this result is that it determines the behavior of $f(x)$ entirely in terms of its behavior at and near $x=0$. (The expansion is valid only under certain conditions of continuity and generally within a restricted range for x.)

Examples

If we take $f(x) = (1+x)^n$ we get the binomial theorem

$$(1+x)^n = 1 + nx + \frac{n(n-1)x^2}{2!} + \frac{n(n-1)(n-2)x^3}{3!} + \cdots$$

For $\sin x$, $\cos x$, e^x we get

$$\sin x = \frac{x}{1} - \frac{x^3}{3!} + \frac{x^5}{5!} - \frac{x^7}{7!} + \cdots$$

$$\cos x = 1 - \frac{x^2}{2!} + \frac{x^4}{4!} - \frac{x^6}{6!} + \cdots$$

$$e^x = 1 + \frac{x}{1} + \frac{x^2}{2!} + \frac{x^3}{3!} + \cdots$$

We give the details in the case $f(x) = \sin x$.

$$f(0) = \sin 0 = 0,$$
$$f'(x) = \cos x, \qquad\qquad f'(0) = \cos 0 = 1,$$
$$f''(x) = -\sin x, \qquad\qquad f''(0) = -\sin 0 = 0,$$
$$f'''(x) = -\cos x, \qquad\qquad f'''(0) = -\cos 0 = -1,$$
$$f^{(4)}(x) = \sin x, \qquad\qquad f^{(4)}(0) = \sin 0 = 0, \text{ etc.}$$

The pattern now repeats itself, and we get the Taylor Series

$$\sin x = 0 + \frac{1x}{1} + \frac{0x^2}{2!} + \frac{-1x^3}{3!} + \frac{0x^4}{4!} + \frac{1x^5}{5!} + \frac{0x^6}{6!} + \cdots$$

$$= x - \frac{x^3}{3!} + \frac{x^5}{5!} - \frac{x^7}{7!} + \cdots.$$

The reader should have no difficulty in deducing the series for $\cos x$ and e^x.

7.13 Trigonometric Functions and the Exponential Function

A good example of the way in which infinite series can shed new light on familiar topics is the fact that the above expansions show a very strong family resemblance among $\sin x$, $\cos x$, e^x, and enable us to express trigonometric functions in terms of exponential functions. This is done by using complex values of the variables. If we take the series for e^x and substitute ix for x, then simplifying and collecting terms in i gives (*Exercise:* verify this)

$$e^{ix} = \cos x + i \sin x. \tag{1}$$

Note that this shows that the familiar DeMoivre's formula

$$(\cos x + i \sin x)^n = \cos nx + i \sin nx$$

amounts to the exponential formula

$$(e^{ix})^n = e^{inx}.$$

By similar means one gets

$$e^{-ix} = \cos x - i \sin x. \tag{2}$$

Solving equations (1) and (2) for $\cos x$ and $\sin x$ gives

$$\cos x = \frac{e^{ix} + e^{-ix}}{2}$$

$$\sin x = \frac{e^{ix} - e^{-ix}}{2i}$$

(note the resemblance to $\cosh x$, $\sinh x$).

A famous equation connecting e, i, and π is got by putting $x = \pi$ in (1). This gives $e^{i\pi} = -1$.

In our work with power series expansions we have proceeded much as the originators in this subject did at first, without much concern for the convergence of the various series to the values of the functions they were claimed to represent. While a thorough study of the problems involved would be too heavy a project for a book such as this, we will, in the following section at least, get a foothold in this direction and gain some appreciation of the methods that are used.

7.14 Taylor's Series (continued)

The expansion $f(x) = f(0) + f'(0)/1\,x + f''(0)/2!\,x^2 + \cdots$ claims to express $f(x)$ in terms of powers of x and the values of $f, f', f'', \ldots$ at $x = 0$ (Fig. 7-4). Sometimes this clearly cannot be done. For example,

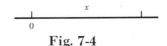

Fig. 7-4

ln $(0) = -\infty$, so one cannot expand ln x in this way. It is natural to try to use some reference point other than 0—that is, to try to express $f(x)$ in terms of powers of $(x-a)$ and the values of $f(x), f'(x), f''(x)$, ... at $x=a$ (Fig. 7-5).

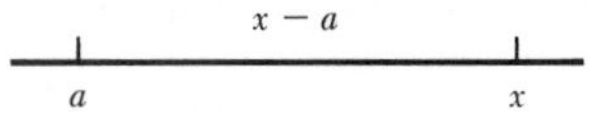

$$\underset{a}{\vdash}\overset{x-a}{\rule{6em}{0pt}}\underset{x}{\dashv}$$

Fig. 7-5

Trying $f(x) = a_0 + a_1(x-a) + a_2(x-a)^2 + \cdots$ and then using the method of Section 7.12 (only setting $x=a$ in order to get terms vanishing at each stage) gives (*Exercise:* verify this)

$$f(x) = f(a) + f'(a)(x-a) + \frac{f''(a)(x-a)^2}{2!} + \frac{f'''(a)(x-a)^3}{3!} + \cdots.$$

This is called the "general Taylor expansion."

We now wish to face the problem of the convergence of the power series to $f(x)$. The trick at the start is to think of wanting the value of $f(x)$ at a *fixed* point, $x=c$, and to treat the "reference" point as variable. To fit this situation we will change our notation and consider expressing $f(c)$ as a power series in $(c-y)$. Thus we exchange the labels

$$a \;\overset{x-a}{\vdash\!\!\!\rule{14em}{0pt}\!\!\!\dashv}\; x$$

for

$$y \;\overset{c-y}{\vdash\!\!\!\rule{14em}{0pt}\!\!\!\dashv}\; c.$$

Our question becomes this: is $f(c)$ equal to

$$f(y) + f'(y)(c-y) + \frac{f''(y)}{2!}(c-y)^2 + \cdots?$$

More precisely, under what conditions does

$$f(c) - \left[f(y) + f'(y)(c-y) + \frac{f''(y)}{2!}(c-y)^2 + \cdots + \frac{f^n(y)(c-y)^n}{n!} \right]$$

approach 0 as n increases beyond all bounds? This expression we call $R_n(y)$—it is the *remainder* left over when we use the first $n+1$

terms of the series to approximate to $f(c)$. $R_n(y)$ has two important properties.

$$R_n(c) = 0 \qquad \text{(obviously)} \tag{1}$$

$$R_n'(y) = 0 - \Big[f'(y) - f'(y) + f''(y)(c-y) - f''(y)(c-y)$$

$$+ \frac{f'''(y)}{2!}(c-y)^2 - \cdots - \frac{f^{[n]}(y)(c-y)^{n-1}}{(n-1)!} + \frac{f^{[n+1]}(y)}{n!}(c-y)^n \Big] \tag{2}$$

and all the terms cancel in pairs except the last. Thus

$$R_n'(y) = -\frac{f^{[n+1]}(y)(c-y)^n}{n!}.$$

It remains to use (1) and (2) to get a workable expression for $R_n(y)$. There are two ways of doing this. First, we can express $R_n(y)$ as a definite integral, namely

$$R_n(y) = \int_c^y \frac{-f^{[n+1]}(t)(c-t)^n}{n!}\, dt$$

[this follows directly from (1), (2) and the Fundamental Theorem]. A more useful form can be obtained, however, by the following argument. Let us suppose that $y < c$, so that as t varies from c to y, $(c-t)$ varies from 0 through negative values to $(c-y)$. Thus for $y < t < c$, and for n odd, $-(c-t)^n/n! > 0$.

If V_1 is the greatest value attained by $f^{[n+1]}(t)$ over the interval $y \leqslant t \leqslant c$ then, for all values of t in this interval,

$$-\frac{(c-t)^n}{n!} f^{[n+1]}(t) \leqslant -\frac{(c-t)^n}{n!} V_1.$$

Similarly, if V_2 is the least such value,

$$-\frac{(c-t)^n}{n!} V_2 \leqslant -\frac{(c-t)^n}{n!} f^{[n+1]}(t).$$

On integrating, these inequalities yield

$$\int_c^y -\frac{(c-t)^n}{n!} f^{[n+1]}(t)\, dt \geqslant \int_c^y -\frac{(c-t)^n}{n!} V_1\, dt$$

and

$$\int_c^y -\frac{(c-t)^n}{n!} V_2\, dt \geqslant \int_c^y -\frac{(c-t)^n}{n!} f^{[n+1]}(t)\, dt.$$

The inequalities get reversed because $c > y$, and thus we are integrating in the "negative" direction. V_1 and V_2 being constant, they can be extracted from both integrations. Hence we get

$$V_1 \int_c^y -\frac{(c-t)^n}{n!}\, dt \leq \int_c^y -\frac{(c-t)^n}{n!} f^{[n+1]}(t)\, dt \leq V_2 \int_c^y -\frac{(c-t)^n}{n!} V_2\, dt.$$

Now V_1, V_2 were values attained by $f^{[n+1]}(t)$. V_2 gave a value greater than the term in the middle, and V_1 gave a value less than this term. Hence some intermediate value V_0 gives exactly this term, for

$$V \int_c^y -\frac{(c-t)^n}{n!}\, dt$$

varies continuously with V and hence must attain all values in between any two attained values. Similarly, if $f^{[n+1]}(t)$ is continuous, then, since V_1 and V_2 are values attained by it, so is the intermediate value, V_0. Thus $V_0 f^{[n+1]}(u)$ for some u between c and y, and

$$f^{[n+1]}(u) \int_c^y -\frac{(c-t)^n}{n!}\, dt = \int_c^y -\frac{(c-t)^n}{n!} f^{[n+1]}(t)\, dt = R_n(y).$$

If $y > c$, or if n is even, the directions of the inequalities get changed but the net result of the above argument is the same. Finally, evaluating

$$\int_c^y -\frac{(c-t)^n}{n!}\, dt$$

we get

$$R_n(y) = f^{[n+1]}(u) \frac{(c-y)^{n+1}}{(n+1)}.$$

Thus, the remainder is like the *next* term in the series (after the terms used in the approximation), only *we compute the $n+1$th derivative* not at y but *at some value between y and c*. This is known as the Lagrange form of the remainder.

Another form, more useful with some functions, is obtained by applying the law of the mean directly to $R_n(y)$. Generally

$$R_n(y) = R_n(c) + (y-c) R_n'(u)$$

where u lies somewhere between y and c. In our case, $R_n(c) = 0$, hence

$$R_n(y) = (y-c) R_n'(u)$$

$$= -(y-c) \frac{f^{[n+1]}(u)(c-u)^n}{n!}$$

$$= (c-y) \frac{f^{[n+1]}(u)(c-u)^n}{n!}$$

It is convenient here to use the ratio $(u-y)/(c-y)=\theta$. Thus, $c-u=(1-\theta)(c-y)$, and $R_n(y)$ becomes

$$\frac{f^{[n+1]}(u)}{n!}(c-y)^{n+1}(1-\theta)^n$$

where $0<\theta<1$. This is known as the Cauchy (pronounced "co-shee") form of the remainder. (Note that the values of u in the two forms need not be the same. Moreover, u and θ will be functions of c, y, and n.)

To justify the Taylor expansion in a particular case, we must show, using one or the other forms of the remainder, that R_n approaches 0 as n increases beyond all bounds. This we now do in a few examples.

7.15 Applications

Our change in notation having served its purpose, let us change back to a and x. Furthermore, we will deal here only with cases where a is taken to be 0. Thus we get remainders of the form

$$\frac{f^{[n+1]}(\theta x)\,x^{n+1}}{(n+1)!} \qquad \text{(Lagrange)},$$

$$\frac{f^{[n+1]}(\theta x)\,x^{n+1}\,(1-\theta)^n}{n!} \qquad \text{(Cauchy)},$$

where $0<\theta<1$ and θ is a function of x and n.

(i) $f(x)=e^x$. Here $f^{[n+1]}(x)=e^x$. Thus the remainder is

$$\frac{e^{\theta x}\,x^{n+1}}{(n+1)!}.$$

$e^{\theta x}$ is bounded as n varies, since $0<\theta<1$. $x^{n+1}/[(n+1)!]$ approaches 0, since

$$\frac{x^{n+2}}{(n+2)!}\cdot\frac{(n+1)!}{x^{n+1}}=\frac{x}{n+2}.$$

Hence the remainder approaches 0 as n increases beyond all bounds, *regardless* of the value of x. Therefore

$$e^x=1+x/1+x^2/2+\cdots$$

for all values of x.

(ii) $f(x)=\sin x$. $f^{[n+1]}(x)$ will always be either $\sin x$ or $\cos x$, hence is bounded. $(x^{n+1})/[(n+1)!]$ approaches 0 as in (i). The same applies to $\cos x$. Hence

$$\sin x=x-\frac{x^3}{3!}+\frac{x^5}{5!}+\cdots$$

for all values of x;

$$\cos x = 1 - \frac{x^2}{2!} + \frac{x^4}{4!} - \cdots$$

for all values of x. [Remember that here, as elsewhere in this book, trigonometric functions are applied to *numbers*, sin (the number x) meaning the same as sin (x radians).]

(iii) $f(x) = (1+x)^m$, where $-1 < x < 1$. (*Exercise:* try using the Lagrange remainder—difficulties will arise). $f^{(n+1)}(x)$ is $m(m-1)(m-2)\cdots(m-n)(1+x)^{m-n-1}$. Thus, the Cauchy remainder is

$$\frac{m(m-1)(m-2)\cdots(m-n)(1+\theta x)^{m-n-1}}{n!} \cdot x^{n+1}(1-\theta)^n$$

$$\frac{m(m-1)\cdots(m-n)x^{n+1}}{n!}$$

goes to 0 since $|x| < 1$ (*Exercise:* show this);

$$(1+\theta x)^{m-n-1} \cdot (1-\theta)^n = (1+\theta x)^{m-1} \cdot \left(\frac{1-\theta}{1+\theta x}\right)^n.$$

$(1+\theta x)^{m-1}$ is bounded, since $0 < \theta < 1$. It remains only to show that $1-\theta < 1+\theta x$, that is, $-\theta < \theta x$, that is, $-1 < x$, which is so.

Thus, for $|x| < 1$ we have justified the familiar binomial expansion. For $x = +1$ or -1, more refined arguments are required.

The above examples are typical of the methods used. Often it is easier to proceed using theorems concerning term-by-term differentiation, but we shall not pursue the subject that far.

Exercises

1. Using the series for $\sin x$, calculate to 4 significant figures $\int_0^1 \sin x^2 \, dx$.

2. Find, to four significant figures $\int_0^1 e^{-x^2} \, dx$.

3. For what values of p does the series $1 + 1/2^p + 1/3^p + \cdots + 1/n^p + \cdots$ diverge?

Problems

4. Show that the series

$$\frac{2}{2 \cdot 3 \cdot 4} + \frac{4}{3 \cdot 4 \cdot 5} + \frac{6}{4 \cdot 5 \cdot 6} + \cdots + \frac{2n}{(n+1)(n+2)(n+3)} + \cdots$$

is convergent.

5. Test the following series for convergence:

(a) $\dfrac{1}{2}+\dfrac{1}{5}+\dfrac{1}{10}+\cdots+\dfrac{1}{1+n^2}+\cdots$,

(b) $\dfrac{1}{2\ln 2}+\dfrac{1}{3\ln 3}+\dfrac{1}{4\ln 4}+\cdots+\dfrac{1}{(n+1)\ln(n+1)}+\cdots$,

(c) $\dfrac{\ln 2}{2}+\dfrac{\ln 3}{3}+\cdots+\dfrac{\ln(n+1)}{n+1}+\cdots$.

6. Produce a series $a_1+a_2+\cdots+a_n+\cdots$ that is convergent but where $\sqrt{a_1}+\sqrt{a_2}+\cdots+\sqrt{a_n}+\cdots$ is divergent.

7. Produce a series $a_1+a_2+\cdots+a_n+\cdots$ that is convergent, but where $1a_1+2a_2+\cdots+na_n+\cdots$ is divergent.

8. Derive the Taylor expansion for $\cosh x$ in powers of x. Get the same result by manipulating the series for e^x, e^{-x}.

9. Repeat Problem 8 only using $\sinh x$.

10. Calculate $\sinh 1/2$ to three significant figures and give an upper bound for the error of the approximation.

11. By an appropriate substitution, derive, from the expansion of $\ln(1+x)$ in powers of x, the expansion of $\ln x$ in powers of $x-1$. Derive the same result by means of the general Taylor expansion for $f(x)$ in powers of $x-a$. For what values of x is it convergent?

12. Expand $\sin x$ in powers of $x-(\pi/4)$. Under what circumstances would this expansion be preferable to that in powers of x? For what values of x is it convergent?

13. Expand $\ln x$ in powers of $x-2$. For what values of x is the series convergent?

14. Evaluate the following to three significant figures:
    (a) $\sin 47°$ (don't forget radian measure),
    (b) $\ln 1.04$,
    (c) $\ln 2.01$ (assume $\ln 2 = 0.6931$).

8

Partial Differentiation

We have now seen enough of calculus to recognize it as an organized whole, made up of differentiation, integration, and the Fundamental Theorem that connects them. What we have seen, however, is only part of a larger structure having the same features. This larger structure is obtained by extending the notions of differentiation and integration to functions of several variables. The results will be analogous to what we have already done, but will bring a far greater variety of applications within our reach.

This chapter deals with differentiation; the next discusses integration; both are rudimentary in treatment.

8.1 Functions of Several Variables

$$f(x,y,z) = x^2 + xy + yz^2,$$
$$p(x,y) = \sin x \cos y,$$
$$G(u,v,w) = e^u \cos v/\ln w$$

are examples of functions of several variables. In fact, most things that concern us are functions of several variables; only by keeping some of those variables fixed are we able to get a function of only one variable. For example, the pressure of a given quantity of gas depends on volume and temperature; altitude on the earth's surface depends on latitude and longitude; barometric pressure depends on position and time; intensity of illumination depends on brightness and distance of source; the distance of (x,y,z) from the origin is $\sqrt{x^2 + y^2 + z^2}$.

8.2 Partial Differentiation

Given a function of one variable $f(x)$, $f'(x)$ denotes the derivative of $f(x)$ with respect to x. The generalization that most immediately suggests itself is that, given a function $f(x,y)$ of two variables, x and y, we may consider the result of *differentiation with respect to x*, treating y like a constant, or *differentiation with respect to y*, treating x like a constant—denoted $f_x(x,y)$, $f_y(x,y)$ respectively. Other notations are $\nabla_x f$, $\nabla_y f$ and $\partial f/\partial x$, $\partial f/\partial y$. For example, if $f(x,y) = x^3 y + xy^2 + y^3$, then

$$f_x(x,y) = 3x^2 y + y^2,$$
$$f_y(x,y) = x^3 + 2xy + 3y^2.$$

More generally, a function $F(x_1, x_2, \ldots, x_n)$ of n variables has n *partial derivatives*, the ith one being $F_{x_i}(x_i, \ldots x_n)$, meaning the result of differentiating in the ordinary way with respect to x_i, treating the other x's as constants. Other notations are $\nabla_{x_i} F$, $\partial F/\partial x_i$.

It remains to show that the concept just defined was worth defining. This will be done by showing that it has properties and interpretations entirely analogous to those of $f'(x)$.

Exercises

1. Given $f(x,y,z) = x^2 z + xy + yz^2$, find
   (a) $f_x(x,y,z)$,   (b) $f_y(x,y,z)$,   (c) $f_z(x,y,z)$.

2. Given $G(x,y) = x^2 e^{y^2}$, find
   (a) $G_x(1,0)$,   (b) $G_y(1,1)$.

3. Given $p(u,v,t) = (u^2 + v^2) \sin t$, find
   (a) $p_u(1,1,\pi/2)$,   (b) $p_t(1,1,\pi)$.

4. Given $z = \dfrac{x^3 - y^3}{xy}$, prove that $x \dfrac{\partial z}{\partial x} + y \dfrac{\partial z}{\partial y} = z$.

5. Given $z = \dfrac{e^{x+y}}{e^x + e^y}$, prove that $\dfrac{\partial z}{\partial x} + \dfrac{\partial z}{\partial y} = z$.

6. Given $z = \dfrac{y^2}{x}$, prove that $x \dfrac{\partial z}{\partial x} + y \dfrac{\partial z}{\partial y} = z$.

7. Given $u = \dfrac{xz + y^2}{yz}$, prove that $x \dfrac{\partial u}{\partial x} + y \dfrac{\partial u}{\partial y} + z \dfrac{\partial u}{\partial z} = 0$.

8.3 Interpretations of Partial Derivatives

Rate of change. If, in $f(x,y)$, we let x alone vary, then $f(x,y)$ changes and $\nabla_x f$ is its rate of change with respect to x. Similarly for y and $\nabla_y f$.

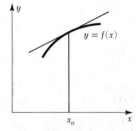

Fig. 8-1

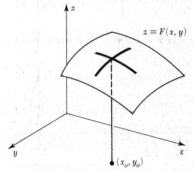

Fig. 8-2

Slope.   Just as $f'(x_0)$ is the slope of the *curve* $y=f(x)$ at $x=x_0$ (Fig. 8-1), so $F_x(x_0,y_0)$ is the slope of the *surface* $z=F(x,y)$ at (x_0,y_0) *in the x-direction*, and $F_y(x_0,y_0)$ is the slope *in the y-direction* (Fig. 8-2).

One might claim that the natural generalization of the slope of a curve at a point is the *steepest* slope of a surface at a point, or a formula for the slope in an arbitrary direction. These, as we shall see, are easily found in terms of F_x, F_y.

A physical example.   Suppose a rectangular plate is heated in such a way that the temperature at (x,y) is a certain function, $T(x,y)$, of x and y (Fig. 8-3). Then $T_x(x_0,y_0)$ is the rate (in degrees Centigrade

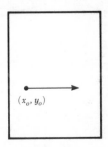

Fig. 8-3

per centimeter, say) at which the temperature is increasing in the positive x-direction at (x_0,y_0), and similarly for $T_y(x_0,y_0)$ and the y-direction.

Exercises

1. Find the slope of the surface $z = 2x^2 + 4y^2$ at the point $(1,1,6)$: (a) in the x-direction, (b) in the y-direction.

2. Find the slope of the surface $z = xy + y^2$ at the point $(2,1,3)$: (a) in the x-direction, (b) in the y-direction.

8.4 Derivatives of Higher Order

Starting with $f(x,y)$, we may differentiate with respect to either x or y. We may then differentiate the result with respect to either x or y, etc. Thus we get not a simple string of derivatives of higher and higher order but an ever branching array of them. Two common notations are shown in Figs 8-4 and 8-5; lines down to the left represent differentiation with respect to x, the others with respect to y.

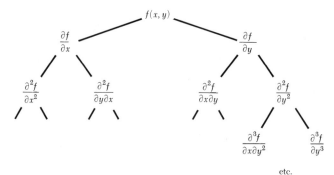

Fig. 8-4

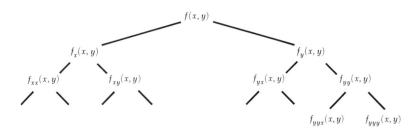

Fig. 8-5

For most functions usually encountered, the order of differentiation doesn't matter. For example $f_{xy} = f_{yx}$. The branching is then somewhat abridged. As an example, consider $f(x,y) = xy \sin xy$.

$$f_x(x,y) = y \sin xy + xy \cos xy \cdot y,$$
$$f_y(x,y) = x \sin xy + xy \cos xy \cdot x,$$
$$f_{xy}(x,y) = y \cos xy \cdot x + \sin xy - xy^2 \sin xy \cdot x + 2xy \cos xy,$$
$$f_{yx}(x,y) = x \cos xy \cdot y + \sin xy - x^2y \sin xy \cdot y + 2xy \cos xy.$$

f_{xy} and f_{yx} are seen to be equal. The notation for functions of three or more variables is similar.

Exercises

1. Given $z = \ln \sqrt{x^2 + y^2}$, prove that $\dfrac{\partial^2 z}{\partial x^2} + \dfrac{\partial^2 z}{\partial y^2} = 0$.

2. Given $a = \dfrac{x+y}{x-y}$, prove that $z_{xy} = z_{yx}$.

3. Given $z = \tan^{-1} \dfrac{y}{x}$, prove that $\dfrac{\partial^2 z}{\partial x^2} + \dfrac{\partial^2 z}{\partial y^2} = 0$.

4. Given $z = \cos(x+y) + \cos(x-y)$, prove that $\dfrac{\partial^2 z}{\partial x^2} - \dfrac{\partial^2 z}{\partial y^2} = 0$.

5. Given $u = \dfrac{1}{\sqrt{x^2 + y^2 + z^2}}$, prove that $\dfrac{\partial^2 u}{\partial x^2} + \dfrac{\partial^2 u}{\partial y^2} + \dfrac{\partial^2 u}{\partial z^2} = 0$.

6. Given $z = \ln(x-y) + \tan(x+y)$, prove that $z_{xx} = z_{yy}$.

7. Given $u = z \tan^{-1} \dfrac{x}{y}$, prove that $\dfrac{\partial^2 u}{\partial x^2} + \dfrac{\partial^2 u}{\partial y^2} + \dfrac{\partial^2 u}{\partial z^2} = 0$.

8.5 Functions of Functions

Next we will derive a generalization of the chain rule of differentiation.

(i) Consider $z = F[x(t), y(t)]$. This is a function of two variables, each of which is a function of t. Thus we have, ultimately, a function of the one variable, t. What is $D_t z$? By definition, $D_t z = \lim_{\Delta t \to 0} \Delta z / \Delta t$. Let us concentrate on Δz.

$$\Delta z = F(x + \Delta x, y + \Delta y) - F(x,y),$$

where Δx and Δy are the changes in x and y due to the change Δt in t. Let us (dropping the role of t for the moment) perform these changes in x and y one at a time, x first. The change in z is then the sum of two changes:

$$\Delta z = F(x + \Delta x, y + \Delta y) - F(x + \Delta x, y) + F(x + \Delta x, y) - F(x,y)$$
$$\text{(change} \qquad\qquad + \qquad\qquad \text{change)}$$

Now we use the law of the mean twice, with y alone varying in the first difference and x in the second, and with F_y, F_x playing the roles of $f'(x)$. This gives

$$\Delta z = F_y(x + \Delta x, y')\, \Delta y + F_x(x', y)\, \Delta x,$$

where $x < x' < x + \Delta x$ and $y < y' < y + \Delta y$. Now, dividing by Δt, we get

$$\frac{\Delta z}{\Delta t} = F_x(x', y)\, \frac{\Delta x}{\Delta t} + F_y(x + \Delta x, y')\, \frac{\Delta y}{\Delta t},$$

which yields (on letting Δt, Δx, Δy approach 0)

$$D_t z = F_x(x,y)\, D_t x + F_y(x,y)\, D_t y,$$

which could also be written

$$D_t z = \nabla_x F D_t x + \nabla_y F\, D_t y.$$

(ii) More generally, consider $z = F[x(r,s),\ y(r,s)]$. Here z is ultimately a function of two variables, r and s. What are $\nabla_r z$, $\nabla_s z$? $\nabla_r z$ means ($D_r z$ where s is kept fixed), which is ($F_x D_r x + F_y D_r y$ where s is kept fixed), which is $F_x \nabla_r x + F_y \nabla_r y$, or $\nabla_x F \nabla_r x + \nabla_y F \nabla_r y$. Similarly $\nabla_s z = F_x \nabla_s x + F_y \nabla_s y$, or $\nabla_x F \nabla_s x + \nabla_y F \nabla_s y$.

Example

Consider $z = (r^2 s)^2 + (rs^2)^2$. We can of course calculate $\nabla_r z$, $\nabla_s z$ directly, but we can also proceed by the method of the present section, treating z as $F(x,y)$, where $F(x,y) = x^2 + y^2$ and $x = r^2 s$, $y = rs^2$. $\nabla_x F$ is then $2x$, and $\nabla_y F$ is $2y$. Also, $\nabla_r x = 2rs$, $\nabla_r y = s^2$, $\nabla_s x = r^2$, $\nabla_s y = 2rs$. Hence

$$\nabla_r z = 2x \cdot 2rs + 2y \cdot s^2$$

and

$$\nabla_s z = 2x \cdot r^2 + 2y \cdot 2rs.$$

Replacing x, y by $r^2 s, rs^2$, respectively, gives the answers in terms of r and s.

These results are easily remembered because the component parts are similar to the usual chain rule—with one part for each variable and partial derivatives in appropriate places. Their value lies not in application to particular cases so much as in their use in proving general theorems, as will be seen. Exactly similar results hold for any number of variables.

Exercises

1. Given $z = \sin xy$, $x = t^2$, $y = 1 + t$, find, by the chain rule, $D_t z$.
2. Given $u = xye^z$, $x = 2t$, $y = \ln t$, $z = t^2$, find, by the chain rule, $D_t u$.
3. Given $u = x^2 - 3xy + y^2$, $x = \cos t$, $y = \sin t$, find $D_t u$.

Problems

4. Just as with functions of one variable, so with functions of several variables—formulas involving derivatives yield approximate formulas for increments. From

$$D_t f[x(t), y(t)] = f_x D_t x + f_y D_t y$$

one gets (in the sense of the relative error approaching 0 as Δ_t approaches 0) the approximation

$$\frac{\Delta f}{\Delta t} \approx f_x \frac{\Delta x}{\Delta t} + f_y \frac{\Delta y}{\Delta t},$$

from which follows $\Delta f \approx f_x \Delta x + f_y \Delta y$.

The diameter and altitude of a right circular cylinder are measured to be 6 inches and 8 inches with a possible error of 0.2 inches. What is the approximate maximum possible error in the computed volume? (Use the approximation formula above.)

5. Given $v = x^2 yz$, where $x = 2$, $y = 4$, $z = 3$, what is the approximate change in v as x, y, z each change by 0.1?

6. The sides of a rectangle are measured to be 7 feet and 12 feet, with possible errors of 1 inch. What is the approximate possible error in the computed area?

7. Express approximately the increments in the following functions in terms of increments in the variables:
   (a) $xy^2 + x^2 y$,   (b) $2xe^y z$,
   (c) $u \sin v + v \cos u$,   (d) $(x^2 + y^4)^6$,
   (e) $xz + y^2 z + x^3 y^2$,   (f) $e^{x/y}$.

8.6 Implicitly Defined Functions

(i) An equation $f(x, y) = 0$ can be thought of as defining y as a function of x. The left side, as in the previous section, part (i), is a function of variables x and y, each of which is thus a function of x. Applying the result of part (i) to both sides yields

$$f_x D_x x + f_y D_x y = 0.$$

But $D_x x = 1$, hence, solving for $D_x y$, we get $D_x y = -f_x/f_y$.

(ii)   Similarly, $f(x,y,z) = 0$ defines z as a function of x and y. Applying the result of the previous section, part (ii), we get

$$f_x \nabla_x x + f_y \nabla_x y + f_z \nabla_x z = 0$$

on differentiating with respect to x. But this involves treating y like a constant. Hence $\nabla_x y = 0$. Solving what is left for $\nabla_x z$ gives $\nabla_x z = -f_x/f_z$. Similarly, $\nabla_y z = -f_y/f_z$.

Examples

(i)   Given $f(x,y) = 0$,   where $f(x,y) = x^2 y + xy + xy^2$,   we   have $f_x = 2xy + y + y^2$, $f_y = x^2 + x + 2xy$; hence

$$D_x y = \frac{-f_x}{f_y} = -\frac{2xy + y + y^2}{x^2 + x + 2xy}.$$

We could have proceeded instead by the method of Section 2.16.

(ii)   Given $f(x,y,z) = 0$, where $f(x,y,z) = xy^2 + yz^2 + zx^2$, we have $f_x = y^2 + 2zx$, $f_y = 2xy + z^2$, $f_z = 2yz + z^2$; hence

$$\nabla_x z = -\frac{y^2 + 2zx}{2yz + x^2}, \quad \nabla_y z = -\frac{2xy + z^2}{2yz + x^2}.$$

Exercises

1. Given $x^3 + 3xy^2 + 2y^2 = 16$, find $D_x y$.

2. Given $xy^2 + x^2 y - 3 = 0$, find $D_x y$.

3. Given $x^2 + 4y^2 + 9z^2 = 36$, find $\partial z/\partial x$, $\partial z/\partial y$.

4. Given $x^4 y + xy^4 + x^2 y^3 = 6$, find $D_x y$.

5. Given $ax^2 + 2bxy + cy^2 + 2dx + 2ey + f = 0$, find $D_x y$.

6. Given $x^{2/3} + y^{2/3} + z^{2/3} = a^{2/3}$, find $\partial y/\partial x$, $\partial y/\partial z$.

7. Given $Ayz + Bzx + Cxy = D$, find $\partial z/\partial x$, $\partial z/\partial y$.

8. Given $Ax^2 + By^2 + Cz^2 = D$, find $\partial z/\partial x$, $\partial z/\partial y$.

Problems

9. Given $f(x,y) = 0$, $g(x,z) = 0$, z being the independent variable, prove that $(\partial g/\partial x)(\partial f/\partial y) D_z y = (\partial f/\partial x)(\partial g/\partial z)$. *Hint:* note that $D_z x = D_y x\, D_z y$.

10. Given $F(x,y,z) = 0$, prove that $(\partial x/\partial y)(\partial y/\partial z)(\partial z/\partial x) = -1$.

8.7 Maxima and Minima

$f(x,y)$ is said to have a *maximum* (minimum) at (x_0,y_0) if its values in some sufficiently small region containing (x_0,y_0) are all less (greater) than $f(x_0,y_0)$. The geometrical picture (Fig. 8-6) is that of

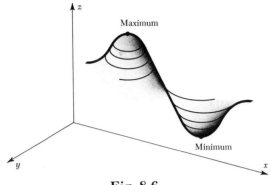

Maximum

Minimum

Fig. 8-6

the top of a hill (or the bottom of a pit). Keeping one variable fixed, we get an ordinary maximum (minimum) in the remaining variable. Hence, at a maximum (minimum),

$$f_x(x_0,y_0) = 0 \quad \text{and} \quad f_y(x_0,y_0) = 0.$$

These conditions do not guarantee a maximum or a minimum. They may, for example, hold at a saddle-point, such as the origin on the surface $z = x^2 - y^2$ (Fig. 8-7). One way of proving that one has a genuine

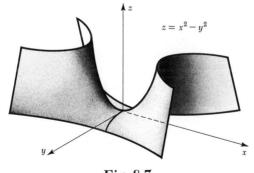

$z = x^2 - y^2$

Fig. 8-7

maximum or minimum is to investigate the slope in an arbitrary direction at the point concerned. This can be handled by using the results of the next section.

Examples

(i)   Find the shortest distance between the straight lines

$$3x = s \qquad x = t$$
$$y = s \qquad y = t$$
$$z = s \qquad 3 - z = t \quad \text{(parameters } s,t\text{)}.$$

Here it is known geometrically that a minimum exists and is actually a least value. The square of the distance between two points, one on each line, is

$$u^2 = \left(\frac{s}{3} - t\right)^2 + (s - t)^2 - (s - 3 + t)^2.$$

This is a function of s and t. At its least value, $\nabla_s u^2 = 0$ and $\nabla_t u^2 = 0$. Thus,

$$\left(\frac{s}{3} - t\right)\frac{1}{3} + (s - t) + (s - 3 + t) = 0$$

and

$$\left(\frac{s}{3} - t\right)(-1) + (s - t)(-1) + (s - 3 + t) = 0.$$

These two equations can now be solved for s and t, from which u can be found.

(ii)   A current I passing through a resistance R generates heat at a rate $I^2 R$ (in suitable units). How should a current divide into three branches of resistances R_1, R_2, R_3 in order to produce minimum heat?

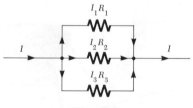

Fig. 8-8

Let the currents in the three branches be I_1, I_2, I_3 (Fig. 8-8). The total rate of heat production is

$$H = I_1^2 R_1 + I_2^2 R_2 + I_3^2 R_3.$$

We now think of trying various combinations of currents in order to get minimum H. Since the total current, $I = I_1 + I_2 + I_3$, is fixed, only two of the I's, say, I_1 and I_2, may be regarded as independent. In terms of these,

$$H = I_1{}^2 R_1 + I_2{}^2 R_2 + (I - I_1 - I_2)^2 R_3.$$

For minimum H, we must have $\nabla_{I_1} H = 0$ and $\nabla_{I_2} H = 0$. The first equation gives

$$2I_1 R_1 + 2(I_1 R_1 + 2(I - I_1 - I_2)(-1) R_3 = 0.$$

Hence

$$I_1 R_1 - I_3 R_3 = 0.$$

Similarly

$$I_1 R_1 - I_2 R_2 = 0.$$

Thus $I_1 R_1 = I_2 R_2 = I_3 R_3$. The point of interest is that this division of currents is what actually takes place. (We have not proved that an actual minimum occurs.)

Problems

1. The distance from the origin to a variable point on the plane $2x + 3y + 6z = 21$ is $\sqrt{x^2 + y^2 + z^2}$. Take x and y as independent and find the point (x,y,z) which minimizes $x^2 + y^2 + z^2$. Show that this yields a minimum distance of 3.

2. Find the shortest distance from the origin to $xyz^2 = 2$.

3. Given a point where $\partial f / \partial x$, $\partial f / \partial y$ are both 0, the function $f(x,y)$ will have at that point a maximum or minimum, provided that

$$\frac{\partial^2 f}{\partial x^2} \frac{\partial^2 f}{\partial y^2} - \left(\frac{\partial^2 f}{\partial x \partial y} \right)^2$$

is positive. It will have a maximum if $\partial^2 f / \partial x^2$ or $\partial^2 f / \partial y^2$ is negative and a minimum if $\partial^2 f / \partial x^2$ or $\partial^2 f / \partial y^2$ is positive. (We shall not prove these results here.)

Find where maxima and minima occur for the following:
(a) $x^2 + xy + y^2 - 6x + 2$,   (b) $x^2 + 2xy + 2y^2 - 6y$,
(c) $x^3 - 3axy + y^3$,   (d) $xy + 1/x + 1/y$.

4. The parametric equations of two curves are $x = p(t)$, $y = q(t)$, $z = r(t)$ and $x = u(s)$, $y = v(s)$, $z = w(s)$. The shortest distance between the two curves will occur where the partial derivatives of $(p - u)^2 + (q - v)^2 + (r - w)^2$ with respect to t, s are both 0. Show from this that the shortest distance is perpendicular to both curves.

5. An open rectangular box has a fixed volume. What shape will yield the minimum surface area?

6. A closed rectangular box has a fixed surface area. What shape yields the maximum volume?

7. An ellipsoid of semi-axes a, b, c has volume $4/3\,\pi\,abc$. If $a+b+c$ is fixed, show that the volume is a maximum if the ellipsoid is a sphere.

8. The bottom of a closed rectangular box costs half as much per unit area as the sides and top. Find the most economical proportions.

8.8 Directional Derivatives: The Gradient

One interpretation we have given of $\nabla_x f(x,y)$ and $\nabla_y f(x,y)$ is that of the slopes of the surface $z=f(x,y)$ in the directions of the x-axis and y-axis. What about slopes in other directions?

If we think in terms of a point (x,y) moving about in the x,y-plane, $\nabla_x z$ and $\nabla_y z$ are derivatives of z with respect to distance measured along the positive x-direction and y-direction, respectively. The natural generalization is that of the *directional derivative*, defined as follows: Let (x,y) start at (x_o,y_o) and travel in the direction of the vector $\bar{v}$ (Fig. 8-9). Then the derivative of z with respect to distance s along this path is called the *directional derivative* of z in the

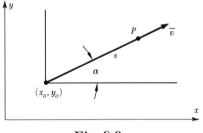

Fig. 8-9

direction of $\bar{v}$ at the point (x_o,y_o), and is denoted by $\nabla_v z$ at (x_o,y_o). We can find the connection with $\nabla_x z$ and $\nabla_y z$ as follows: the coordinates of P are

$$x=x_o+s\cos\alpha,$$
$$y=y_o+s\sin\alpha,$$

where α is as shown in Fig. 8-10 (x_0,y_0 and α are fixed). Thus $\nabla_v z$, which is $D_s z$, is equal to

$$D_s f(x_o+s\cos\alpha,\ y_o+s\sin\alpha)$$
$$=f_x D_s x+f_y D_s y$$
$$=f_x\cos\alpha+f_y\sin\alpha.$$

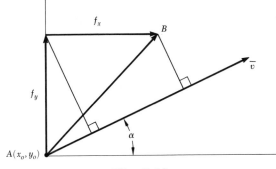

Fig. 8-10

But this is the length of the projection of the vector $\overrightarrow{AB}$, with x,y components $f_x(x_o,y_o)$, $f_y(x_o,y_o)$ on the direction of $\bar{v}$ (Fig. 8-10). This vector, $\overrightarrow{AB}$, is *fixed*, independent of $\bar{v}$: it is called the *gradient* vector of $f(x,y)$ at (x_o,y_o) and is denoted ∇f or grad f. Thus $\nabla_v f$ is the $\bar{v}$ component of ∇f, and, in particular $\nabla_x f$, $\nabla_y f$ are the x and y components of ∇f [all computed at (x_o,y_o)].

We also have the further result that the directional derivative is greatest in the direction of ∇f itself, and that this greatest magnitude is $\sqrt{f_x^2 + f_y^2}$.

As the point (x,y) moves along the line of $\bar{v}$, the situation reduces essentially to that of a function of a single variable, s. For example, if we have a minimum at (x_o,y_o), we know that $D_s z = 0$ and that $D_s^2 z \geqslant 0$.

It should be mentioned, even though we are not attempting to deal with the finer points of such discussions, that a function $f(x,y)$ can have derivatives in the x and y directions and yet fail to have derivatives at all in certain directions. Even if it has derivatives in all directions at a given point, the equation $\nabla_v z = f_x \cos \alpha + f_y \sin \alpha$ may fail to hold for all directional derivatives at that point, and so there may not be any vector with the properties of grad f. In such a case $\nabla_v z$ may not be regarded as the $\bar{v}$ component of some ∇f.

Such things may happen when f_x, f_y fail to be continuous. Figure 8-11 shows what such a surface $z = f(x,y)$ may look like. The offending

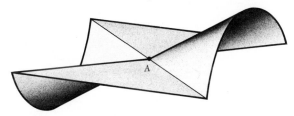

Fig. 8-11

point is A. We say that the surface is *non-differentiable* at A. We have assumed in our arguments that all functions mentioned are differentiable.

Exercises

1. Given $T = 50y/(x^2 + y^2)$, find the rate of change of T at (4,2) in the direction $\alpha = \tan^{-1} - (3/4)$.

2. A function $T(x,y)$ is defined by the value $x^2 + y^2$ at (x,y) in the x,y plane.
   (a) Find the rate of change of T at (3,4) in the direction toward the origin.
   (b) Find the rate of change at (1,5) in the direction making an angle of 30° with the positive x-direction.

3. Given $V = \ln \sqrt{x^2 + y^2}$, find the derivative of V at (3,4) in the direction making an angle of 30° with the positive x-direction.

4. Show that $f(x,y)$ has zero directional derivative in the direction for which $\tan \alpha = -f_x/f_y$.

5. In what direction from (x,y) is the directional derivative of axy a maximum, and what is this maximum value?

6. In Exercise 3, find the magnitude of the maximum rate of change of V and the direction in which it occurs.

7. Find the directional derivative of $e^x \cos y$ at $(1,\pi/4)$ in the direction making an angle of 30° with the positive x-direction.

8.9 The Normal to a Surface: Tangent Planes

We conclude this chapter by seeing how partial derivatives may be used to find normals and tangent planes to surfaces in space. First we deal with the question of tangent lines to curves in space, involving only ordinary derivatives.

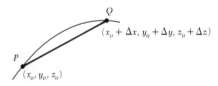

Fig. 8-12

Consider a curve in space

$$x = f(t),$$
$$y = g(t),$$
$$z = h(t),$$

and points P, Q on it (Fig. 8-12). As Q approaches P, the direction of PQ approaches that of the tangent at P. Δx, Δy, Δz are a set of direction numbers of PQ, hence $\Delta x/\Delta t$, $\Delta y/\Delta t$, $\Delta z/\Delta t$ are also. As Δt approaches 0, so do the other Δ's, and PQ approaches tangency. Hence $D_t x$, $D_t y$, $D_t z$ are *direction numbers of the tangent at P*. This yields

$$\frac{x - x_o}{f'(t_o)} = \frac{y - y_o}{g'(t_o)} = \frac{z - z_o}{h'(t_o)}$$

as equations of the tangent line at P (t_o corresponds to P).

We can now find the normal to a surface. Instead of taking the equation of the surface in the form $z = f(x,y)$, we will use the more general form $F(x,y,z) = 0$.

Consider an arbitrary curve

$$x = x(t),$$
$$y = y(t),$$
$$z = z(t),$$

on the surface and through P (Fig. 8-13). Since the curve lies on the

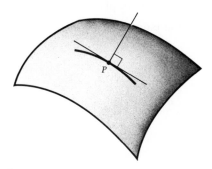

Fig. 8-13

surface, we have

$$F[x(t), y(t), z(t)] = 0.$$

Differentiating with respect to t, we have

$$F_x D_t x + F_y D_t y + F_z D_t z = 0.$$

Now F_x, F_y, F_z, (computed at P) are direction numbers of some direction. Our last equation tells us that this direction is perpendicular to the direction with direction numbers $D_t x$, $D_t y$, $D_t z$. But this direction is tangent to the curve on the surface through P; hence we have a direction that is perpendicular to all tangents through P—that is, we have the normal at P. To sum up, F_x, F_y, F_z *are direction numbers of the normal to the surface* $F(x,y,z) = 0$. This gives $F_x(x - x_o)$

$+F_y(y-y_o)+F_z(z-z_o)=0$ as the equation of the tangent plane at (x_o, y_o, z_o). For example, let us find the equation of the tangent plane to the surface $xy+2yz+4zx-19=0$ at $(1,1,3)$ on it. We have

$$F(x,y,z)=xy+2yz+4zx-19,$$
$$F_x=y+4z=13 \quad \text{at } (1,1,3),$$
$$F_y=x+2z=7 \quad \text{at } (1,1,3),$$
$$F_z=2y+4x=6 \quad \text{at } (1,1,3).$$

The required equation is therefore

$$13(x-1)+7(y-1)+6(z-3)=0.$$

Exercises

1. Find the equation of the tangent plane to $x^2+y^2+z^2=49$ at $(6,2,3)$.

2. Find the equation of the tangent plane to $x^2+xy^2+y^3+z+1=0$ at $(2,-3,4)$.

3. Find the equation of the tangent plane to $x^2+y^2+9z^2=56$ at $(4,2,-2)$.

4. Find the equation of the tangent plane to $x^2y^2+z^2=20$ at $(-1,2,4)$.

5. Find the equation of the tangent plane to $xy+yz+zx=11$ at $(1,2,3)$.

9

Multiple Integration

9.1 From Single Integrals to Double Integrals

The single integral was defined as follows: given a function $f(x)$ of *one* variable and a *one*-dimensional region (a,b), we break the region into little regions having *length* Δx, take a point (x) in each, and form the product $f(x)\,\Delta x$ (Fig. 9-1). Next we add up all such

Fig. 9-1

products, one for each little region, getting $\sum_{a}^{b} f(x)\,\Delta x$; finally, we take the limit of this sum as the decomposition of the original interval gets finer and finer—that is, we find $\lim_{\delta \to 0} \sum_{a}^{b} f(x)\,\Delta x$ where δ is the maximum allowable Δx at each stage.

The double integral we now define as follows: we are given a function $f(x,y)$ of *two* variables, and a *two*-dimensional region, R. We break the region into little regions, a typical region having *area* ΔA (Fig. 9-2), take a point, (x,y) in each, and form the product $f(x,y)\,\Delta A$. Next, we add up all such products, one for each little region, getting $\sum_{R} f(x,y)\,\Delta A$; finally, we take the limit of this sum as the de-

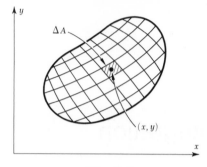

Fig. 9-2

composition of the original region gets finer and finer—that is, we find $\lim_{\delta \to 0} \sum_{R} f(x,y) \, \Delta A$ where δ is the maximum allowable diameter of the little regions at each stage. The role of δ requires the little regions of area to shrink to *points*, not allowing the result shown in Fig. 9-3, for example, where the regions shrink to an *arc*.

Fig- 9-3

Both integrals may be interpreted as masses of regions of varying density. For the single integral, imagine a thin wire of varying linear density, $f(x)$, stretched along the x-axis from $x=a$ to $x=b$. Its total mass will be the single integral. For the double integral, imagine a thin plate of varying areal density, $f(x,y)$, shaped to fit the region R. Its total mass will be the double integral. (The reasoning in both cases is as in Section 4.1.)

9.2 The Double Integral in Cartesian Coordinates

In practice, we subdivide the region of integration in a systematic manner, by means of curves along which one variable is fixed. Consider, for example, a region bounded by curves $y=f(x)$, $y=g(x)$, $x=a$, and $x=b$, and let $F(x,y)$ be the function to be integrated (Fig. 9-4).

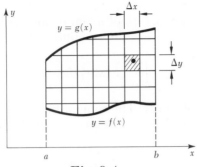

Fig. 9-4

We subdivide the region by lines drawn parallel to the x and y axes. Apart from the regions bounded in part by the curves $y=f(x)$, $y=g(x)$ (whose total contribution will be very small as the decomposition becomes very fine) the subregions will be little rectangles of sides Δx, Δy as shown, and hence of area $\Delta y \cdot \Delta x$, and giving a contribution $F(x,y) \Delta y \cdot \Delta x$ to the integral. The contribution of a typical column is written as

$$\sum_{f(x)}^{g(x)} F(x,y)\,\Delta y \cdot \Delta x,$$

and, adding the contributions of all the columns, we get

$$\sum_{a}^{b} \left[\sum_{f(x)}^{g(x)} F(x,y)\,\Delta y \cdot \Delta x\right].$$

Finally, taking the limit as $\delta \to 0$ (and hence Δx, $\Delta y \to 0$) we get

$$\lim_{\Delta x, \Delta y \to 0} \sum_{a}^{b} \left[\sum_{f(x)}^{g(x)} F(x,y)\,\Delta y \cdot \Delta x\right].$$

For each column sum, Δx is fixed and can hence be extracted as a common factor. Thus we get

$$\lim_{\Delta x, \Delta y \to 0} \sum_{a}^{b} \left[\sum_{f(x)}^{g(x)} F(x,y)\,\Delta y\right] \Delta x.$$

Let us allow·Δy, Δx to approach 0 in turn. The integral can be written

$$\lim_{\Delta x \to 0} \sum_{a}^{b} \left[\lim_{\Delta y \to 0} \sum_{f(x)}^{g(x)} F(x,y)\,\Delta y\right] \Delta x.$$

The interior sum sums over a column, with fixed x. Thus $F(x,y)$ is (for the time being) a function of y alone, and $f(x)$, $g(x)$, are temporarily fixed. The interior limit thus amounts to

$$\int_{f(x)}^{g(x)} F(x,y)\, dy,$$

which is a function of x only. The remaining limit of a sum is then the definite integral of this function. Thus we finally get

$$\int_{a}^{b} \int_{f(x)}^{g(x)} F(x,y)\, dy\, dx,$$

and the evaluation of the double integral is reduced to two successive single integrations. (The brackets are usually omitted in the notation.)

9.3 The Double Integral as the Volume under a Surface

$F(x,y)\Delta A$ can be interpreted as the volume of the column indicated in Fig. 9-5 (approximately), which gives the interpretation of the

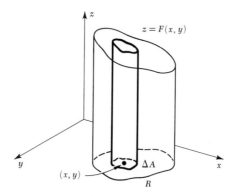

Fig. 9-5

double integral as the *total volume under the surface* $z=F(x,y)$ *and directly above the region R*. This gives an alternative derivation of the result in the preceding section, for the volume is (by the method of Section 6.5) $\int_{a}^{b} A(x)\, dx$, and $A(x)$ is $\int_{f(x)}^{g(x)} F(x,y)\, dy$, since it is the shaded area (as seen projected onto the y, z-plane, Figs. 9-6 and 9-7).

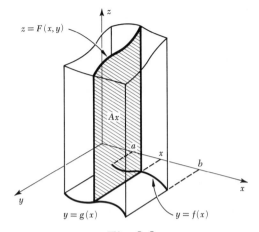

Fig. 9-6

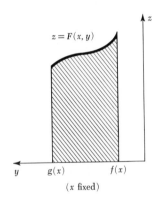

Fig. 9-7

Example

Let us find the volume cut off from the cylinder $x^2+y^2=1$ by the planes $x+y+z=2$, $z=0$. The region of integration is the circle $x^2+y^2=1$ in the x,y-plane. $-\sqrt{1-x^2}$, $+\sqrt{1-x^2}$ here play the roles of $f(x)$, $g(x)$, and -1, $+1$ those of a and b. The required volume is (Fig. 9-8)

$$\int_{-1}^{1}\int_{-\sqrt{1-x^2}}^{\sqrt{1-x^2}} (2-x-y)\, dy\, dx$$

$$= \int_{-1}^{1} 2y - xy - \frac{y^2}{2} \Big|_{-\sqrt{1-x^2}}^{+\sqrt{1-x^2}} dx$$

$$= \int_{-1}^{1} (4\sqrt{1-x^2} - 2x\sqrt{1-x^2})\, dx = 2\pi.$$

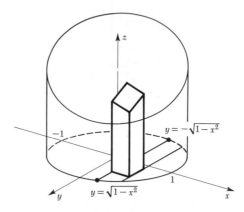

Fig. 9-8

9.4 Moments, Centroids, etc., of a Given Region

Many quantities connected with a given region can be evaluated by a single integration. Because the elements of area are strips, some care must be taken, and only the simpler quantities can be found.

With double integration, the elements of area are not strips of finite length but little pieces that shrink to *points* during the limiting process. This makes for greater uniformity of method and enables us to do far more.

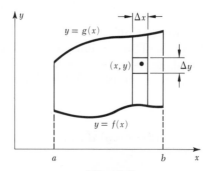

Fig. 9-9

We can find many quantities connected with the region shown in Fig. 9-9 by choosing suitable functions $F(x,y)$ in the integral

$$\int_a^b \int_{f(x)}^{g(x)} F(x,y)\, dy\, dx.$$

(In the following, x and y are the coordinates of a suitably chosen point inside the little region ΔA.)

(a) For the area A of the region, we demand of each little rectangle only its area, $\Delta y\, \Delta x$. Hence we take $F = 1$.

(b) The moments of the little rectangle about the x and y axes are $y\Delta y\Delta x$ and $x\Delta y\Delta x$, respectively. Hence, for M_x, M_y we take $F = y$, $F = x$, respectively.

(c) The coordinates of the centroid are M_y/A, M_x/A, got from (a) and (b).

(d) For moments of inertia, we have the same moment arms as before, only we square them. Hence for I_x, I_y, I_o we take $F = y^2$, $F = x^2$, $F = x^2 + y^2$ (I_o being the moment of inertia about the origin).

(e) We can even throw in a density function, $w(x,y)$, for good measure. The mass of the little rectangle is then $w(x,y)\, \Delta y\, \Delta x$, and we multiply this by the appropriate moment arm (or same squared) as above. Thus we get the same as above, with an extra factor $w(x,y)$ in the integrand. For the total mass, we take $F = w(x,y)$.

(f) If the given region (assuming that it does not intersect the axis) is rotated about the x-axis, the little rectangle travels a distance $2\pi y$ and hence sweeps out a volume $2\pi y\, \Delta y\, \Delta x$. Thus for total volume, we take $F = 2\pi y$. For rotation about the y-axis, take $F = 2\pi x$.

9.5 The Double Integral in Polar Coordinates

Doing to our polar coordinates exactly what we did to the Cartesian coordinates in Section 9.2, we get a subdivision as in Fig. 9-10. The

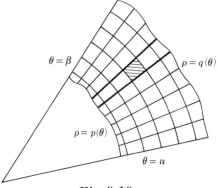

Fig. 9-10

dividing curves are straight lines through the origin (on which θ is fixed) and circles with center at the origin (on which ρ is fixed). The region is bounded by the curves $\rho = p(\theta)$, $\rho = q(\theta)$ and the lines $\theta = \alpha$, $\theta = \beta$.

The little elements of area we consider to be rectangles of sides $\rho\Delta\theta$ and $\Delta\rho$, and area $p\Delta\theta\,\Delta\rho$ (Fig. 9-11). [By considering the element

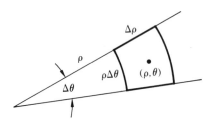

Fig. 9-11

of area as the difference of two circular sectors, the area can be shown to be exactly $\rho\Delta\theta \cdot \Delta\rho$ for some interior point (ρ,θ). This would justify our result.] Integrating a function, $G(\rho,\theta)$ gives

$$\int_\alpha^\beta \int_{p(\theta)}^{q(\theta)} G(\rho,\theta)\,\rho d\rho d\theta,$$

where the order of integration is indicated by heavy lines in Fig. 9-10.

If the region is shaped as follows, then we integrate first with respect to θ and get

$$\int_a^b \int_{f(\rho)}^{g(\rho)} G(\rho,\theta)\,\rho d\theta\, d\rho.$$

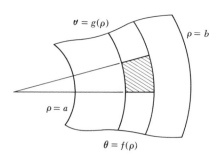

Fig. 9-12

The results of Section 9.4 are obtained in the same way, using $\rho\cos\theta$, $\rho\sin\theta$, ρ, for x and y and $\sqrt{x^2+y^2}$ (Fig. 9-13).

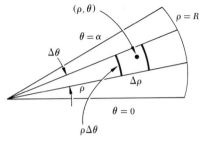

Fig. 9-13

As an example, let us consider the circular sector bounded by the lines $\theta = 0$, $\theta = \alpha$ and the indicated arc of the circle $\rho = R$. Let us find the moment of inertia of this sector about the line $\theta = 0$.

A typical little region, containing a point (ρ, θ), has area $\rho \Delta \rho \Delta \theta$ (for suitably chosen ρ this will be exact; due to the limiting process of integration only an approximation is actually needed). Its distance from $\theta = 0$ is approximately $\rho \sin \theta$: hence its moment of inertia about this line is

$$\rho^2 \sin^2\theta \rho \Delta\rho \Delta\theta = \rho^3 \sin^2\theta \Delta\rho \Delta\theta.$$

Taking the limit of the sum, getting first the contribution of a typical sector as shown and then adding up the contributions of these sectors, we get the integral

$$\int_0^\alpha \int_0^R \rho^3 \sin^2 \theta \, d\rho \, d\theta = \int_0^\alpha \sin^2 \theta \left. \frac{\rho^4}{4} \right|_0^R \, d\theta$$

$$= \int_0^\alpha \frac{R^4}{4} \sin^2 \theta \, d\theta$$

$$= \frac{R^4}{4} \int_0^\alpha \frac{1 - \cos 2\theta}{2} \, d\theta$$

$$= \frac{R^4}{8} \left[\theta - \frac{1}{2} \sin 2\theta \right]_0^\alpha$$

$$= \frac{R^4}{8} \left[\alpha - \frac{1}{2} \sin 2\alpha \right].$$

Other quantities connected with this region can equally easily be found. To find the moment of inertia about the line $\theta = \pi/2$, one multiplies $\rho \, \Delta\rho \, \Delta\theta$ by the square of the distance, $\rho \cos \theta$, from (ρ, θ) to this line. This yields the integral

$$\int_0^\alpha \int_0^R \rho^3 \cos^2 \theta \, d\rho \, d\theta.$$

If moments are wanted, $\rho \sin \theta$, $\rho \cos \theta$ are used instead of their squares.

To find the volume generated by rotating the sector about the line $\theta = 0$, one reasons that each little region generates a volume of (approximately) its area times the distance it travels—that is, $\rho\,\Delta\rho\,\Delta\theta$ times $2\pi\rho\sin\theta$. Thus one gets an integral

$$\int_0^\alpha \int_0^R 2\pi\rho\sin\theta\,\rho\,d\rho d\theta.$$

9.6 Changing from One Coordinate System to Another

Sometimes an integral that is very difficult to work out in Cartesian coordinates can be worked out very easily in polar form (and vice versa). This is due not merely to the change of variables from x, y to ρ, θ but to the fact that *a different method of subdivision is used*. An example will illustrate the point.

Consider

$$\int_0^a \int_0^{\sqrt{a^2-x^2}} \sqrt{a^2-x^2-y^2}\,dy\,dx$$

(lengthy to work out). From the limits of integration, we see that the region of integration is bounded by the curves $y=0$, $y=\sqrt{(a^2-x^2)}$, $x=0$, $x=a$, and hence is the first quadrant of the circle $x^2+y^2=a^2$ (Fig. 9-14), where the Cartesian method of subdivision is indicated.

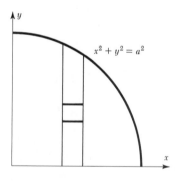

Fig. 9-14

Using polar coordinates, we have a different subdivision (Fig. 9-15).

Integral $= \displaystyle\int_0^{\pi/2}\int_0^a \sqrt{a^2-\rho^2}\,\rho\,d\rho\,d\theta$, which works out easily, thanks to the presence of the factor ρ.

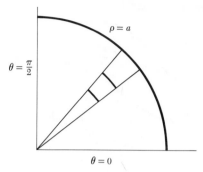

$$\rho = a$$

$$\theta = \frac{\pi}{2}$$

$$\theta = 0$$

Fig. 9-15

9.7 The Existence of a Centroid

The characteristic property of the centroid of a given region is that it is a point C such that, given *any* line L, the total moment about L of the region is its area multiplied by the distance of C from L (Fig. 9-16). Thinking in terms of a mass distribution of unit density over the region, this means that *for purposes of finding moments*, one may assume the mass to be concentrated at C. *It is not at all obvious that such a point exists.* The usual method of finding the centroid consists of finding a point that has the required property with respect to the x and y axes. One then assumes that it has this property with respect to any line. It is this assumption that must be justified.

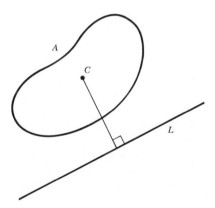

A

C

L

Fig. 9-16

Let $(\bar{x}, \bar{y})$ have the property that, for the region R of area A, $M_x = \bar{y}A$, $M_y = \bar{x}A$ (Fig. 9-17). Let $ax + by + c = 0$ be any straight line in normalized form $(a^2 + b^2 = 1)$. Then the distance of any point

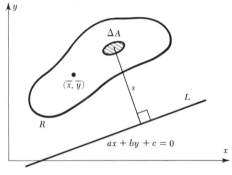

Fig. 9-17

(x,y) from this line is $s=ax+by+c$. The *proof* of our assumption is as follows (assuming the distributive property of the double integral):

$$M_L=\int_R s\,dA=\int_R (ax+by+c)\,dA$$

$$=\int_R ax\,dA+\int_R by\,dA+\int_R c\,dA$$

$$=a\,A\,\bar{x}+b\,A\,\bar{y}+cA$$

$$=A\,(a\bar{x}+b\bar{y}+c)$$

$$=A\,(\text{distance of centroid from } L).$$

9.8 Triple Integrals

The extension from double integrals to triple integrals proceeds exactly as in the extension from single integrals to double integrals. We shall omit the details and simply sketch the derivation of the main results.

Three kinds of coordinate systems are in common use to locate points in three-dimensional space (see Figs. 9-18, 9-19, and 9-20). In each case the space is decomposed by means of surfaces on which one coordinate is fixed. In the Cartesian case this yields planes parallel to the three coordinate planes. In the cylindrical case the surfaces $\rho=K$ are cylinders, the surfaces $\theta=K$ are planes through the vertical axis, and the surfaces $z=K$ are horizontal planes. In the spherical case, $\rho=K$ yields spheres, $\theta=K$ yields planes through the vertical axis, and $\theta=K$ yields cones with axis the vertical axis. The corresponding elements of volume are shown in Figs. 9-21, 9-22, and 9-23.

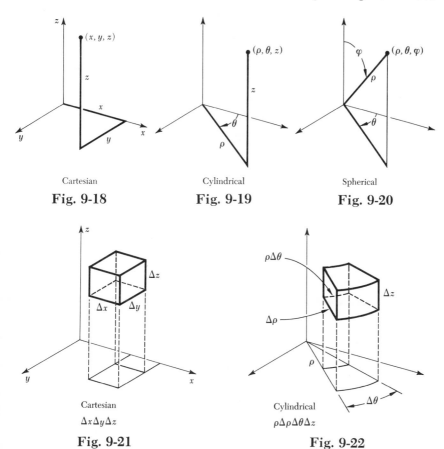

Cartesian
Fig. 9-18

Cylindrical
Fig. 9-19

Spherical
Fig. 9-20

Cartesian
$\Delta x \Delta y \Delta z$
Fig. 9-21

Cylindrical
$\rho \Delta \rho \Delta \theta \Delta z$
Fig. 9-22

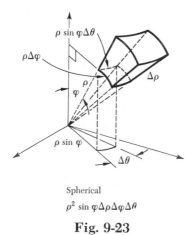

Spherical
$\rho^2 \sin \varphi \Delta \rho \Delta \varphi \Delta \theta$
Fig. 9-23

Examples

We shall express the moment of inertia about the z-axis of the upper hemisphere of $x^2 + y^2 + z^2 = 1$ as a triple integral in three ways. In Cartesian coordinates (Fig. 9-24),

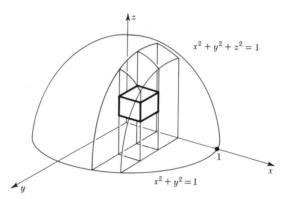

Fig. 9-24

$$I = 4 \int_0^1 \int_0^{\sqrt{1-x^2}} \int_0^{\sqrt{1-x^2-y^2}} (x^2 + y^2)\ dz\ dy\ dx.$$

The innermost integration gives the contribution of the column, the next gives that of the slice, and the last sums over all the slices. The total contribution is four times that of the first octant.

In cylindrical coordinates (Fig. 9-25),

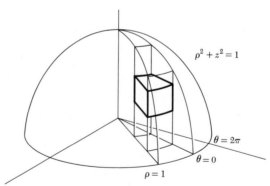

Fig. 9-25

$$I = \int_0^{2\pi} \int_0^1 \int_0^{\sqrt{1-\rho^2}} \rho^2 \rho\ dz\ d\rho\ d\theta.$$

The innermost integration gives the contribution of the column, the next gives that of the wedge, and the last sums over the wedges all the way around.

In spherical coordinates (Fig. 9-26),

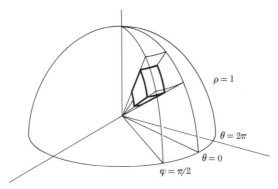

Fig. 9-26

$$I = \int_0^{2\pi} \int_0^{\pi/2} \int_0^1 \rho^2 \sin^2\phi \, d\rho \, d\phi \, d\theta.$$

The innermost integration gives the contribution of the "ray," the next gives that of the wedge, and the last sums over the wedges all the way around.

Exercises

Evaluate the following integrals, sketching the regions of integration.

1. $\int_0^1 \int_2^3 x + y \, dy \, dx.$

2. $\int_0^4 \int_0^x y \, dy \, dx.$

3. $\int_1^2 \int_0^{2y} x^3 y \, dx \, dy.$

4. $\int_0^a \int_0^{\sqrt{x}} 1 \, dy \, dx.$

5. $\int_0^1 \int_0^x e^{x+y} \, dy \, dx.$

6. $\int_0^2 \int_0^y xy \, dx \, dy.$

7. $\int_0^\pi \int_0^{a(1+\cos\theta)} \rho^2 \sin\theta \, d\rho \, d\theta.$

8. $\int_0^{\pi/2} \int_{a\cos\theta}^a \rho^4 \, d\rho \, d\theta.$

Integrate the following functions over the indicated regions.

9. 1 over the region bounded by $x^2 - y^2 = a^2$ and $x = 2a$.

10. 1 over the region bounded by $y^2 = 4x$ and $2x + y - 4 = 0$.

11. $x + y$ over the region in Exercise 10 above.

12. $y - x$ over the triangle bounded by $x = 1$, $y = 0$, $y = x$.

13. $x^2 + y^2$ over the region bounded by $y = x$ and $y^2 = 4x$.

14. $\rho \cos \theta$ over the first quadrant sector bounded by $\theta = 0$, $\theta = \alpha$, $\rho = R$.

15. $\sin \theta$ over the circle $\rho = a \cos \theta$.

16. $\rho^2 - \rho a$ over one loop of $\rho = a \cos 2\theta$.

Problems

17. Find the volume generated by revolving the cardiod $\rho = a(1 + \cos \theta)$ about the line $\theta = 0$.

18. Find the centroid of a semicircular area.

19. Find the moment of inertia with respect to the line $y = x$ of the area bounded by $y = x^2$, $x = y^2$.

20. Find the centroid of one quadrant of the elliptical area $x^2/a^2 + y^2/b^2 = 1$.

21. Find the volume generated by rotating about the x-axis the region bounded by $2y = x^3$, $y^2 = 8x$.

22. For the region bounded by $y^2 - x^2 = 1$, $x = 2y - 2$ find (a) its moment about each axis; (b) its moment of inertia about each axis; and (c) the volume generated by rotating it about each axis.

23. Evaluate $\displaystyle\int_0^{\pi/4} \int_0^{1/\cos\theta} \rho \, d\rho \, d\theta$ (a) as it stands; and (b) by converting to Cartesian coordinates.

24. Find the area inside the circle $\rho = 2a \cos \theta$ and outside the circle $\rho = a$.

25. Evaluate $\displaystyle\int_{-1}^{1} \int_{-\sqrt{a^2-x^2}}^{\sqrt{a^2-x^2}} x^2 + y^2 \, dy \, dx$ by converting to polar coordinates.

26. Find the volume under the surface $z = x^2 + y^2$ and directly above the circle $x^2 + y^2 = 2x$.

27. Find the volume bounded by the plane $x/a + y/b + z/c = 1$ and the coordinate planes.

28. Find the moment of inertia about the z axis of the region in Problem 27 above.

Answers to Odd-Numbered Exercises and Problems

Chapter 1

EXERCISES

1. 0.8414, 0.9549, 0.9996, 1.0000.   **3.** 2.250, 2.594, 2.704; using the first four terms, 2.250, 2.570, 2.657.   **5.** 2.5, 2.8.

PROBLEMS

7. (a) .44 ft., 2.2 ft./sec.,   (b) $2K+K^2$ ft., $2+K$ ft./sec.   **9.** (a) 1.20, 1.35, $\frac{3}{2}\frac{(K-1)}{K}$, (b) $\frac{3}{2}$.   **11.** (a) 75, (b) 75.   **13.** (a) 1, (b) 1, (c) 1, (d) 0, (e) 1, (f) 1; (a^1) 0, (b^1) 0, (c^1) 0, (d^1) -1, (e^1) -1, (f^1) -1.

Chapter 2

Section 2.3   EXERCISES

1. (a) $\lim\limits_{h\to 0}\dfrac{(x+h)^3-x^3}{h}=3x^2$,   (b) $\lim\limits_{h\to 0}\dfrac{(x+h)^2+(x+h)^3-x^2-x^3}{h}=2x+3x^2$, (c) $\lim\limits_{h\to 0}\dfrac{5(x+h)^2+2(x+h)^3-5x^2-2x^3}{h}=10x+6x^2$.

Section 2.4   EXERCISES

1. (a) 4, (b) 12, (c) $\dfrac{1}{4}$, (d) $1-3K^2$.

PROBLEMS

3. (a) 1, (b) -1, (c) 1 if $h \to 0+$, -1 if $h \to 0-$, generally no limit exists.
5. (b) $D_x(f_1 \cdot f_2 \cdot f_3 \cdots f_n) = D_x f_1 \cdot f_2 \cdot f_3 \cdots f_n + f_1 \cdot D_x f_2 \cdot f_3 \cdots f_n + f_1 \cdot f_2 \cdot D_x f_3$
$\cdots f_n + \cdots + f_1 \cdot f_2 \cdot f_3 \cdots D_x f_n$.

Section 2.5   PROBLEMS

1. (a) Proceed by induction. Differentiate the given (supposed valid) formula
for $D_x{}^n(u \cdot v)$. Use the result that $C(n,r) + C(n,r+1) = C(n+1,r+1)$.
(b) $D_x{}^6 u \cdot v + 6 D_x{}^5 u \cdot D_x v + 15 D_x{}^4 u \cdot D_x{}^2 v + 20 D_x{}^3 u \cdot D_x{}^3 v + 15 D_x{}^2 u \cdot D_x{}^4 v$
$+ 6 D_x u \cdot D_x{}^5 v + u D_x{}^6 v$.

Section 2.6   EXERCISES

1. (a) $3 + 2x$, (b) $3 + 2t$, (c) $3 + 2x^2$, (d) $1/(1-\theta)^2$.

Section 2.7   EXERCISES

1. (a) $(0,0)$, $(\sqrt{6},0)$, $(-\sqrt{6},0)$;   (b) $(0,0)$, $(\sqrt{3},-9)$, $(-\sqrt{3},-9)$;
(c) $(1,-5)$, $(-1,-5)$.

Section 2.8   EXERCISES

1. (a) $21(2x - 5x^3)^{20}$, (b) $\dfrac{-9 \cdot 2t}{(1+t^2)^{10}}$,

(c) $\dfrac{(1-y^2)2 - (2y+9)(-2y)}{(1-y^2)^2}$, (d) $\dfrac{3x^2 + 4x}{2}$.

Section 2.10   EXERCISES

1. (a) $\dfrac{2}{3} x^{-1/3}$,

(b) $\dfrac{7}{5} x^{2/5}$,

(c) $\dfrac{-4}{3} z^{-7/3}$,

(d) $\dfrac{1}{2\sqrt{u}}$,

(e) $\dfrac{1}{3}(1 + \sqrt{x})^{-2/3} \cdot \dfrac{1}{2\sqrt{x}}$.

Section 2.12   EXERCISES

1. (a) $17(x^2 + 3x)^{16} \cdot (2x + 3)$, (b) $257(1 + 9x^3)^{256} \cdot 27x^2$,

(c) $\dfrac{-72(2x+9)}{(x^2 + 9x)^{73}}$,

(d) $3 \cos 3x$, (e) $2x \sec^2(1 + x^2)$,

(f) $-\sin \sqrt{x} \cdot \dfrac{1}{2\sqrt{x}} + 2x \cdot 4 \cos x^2,$

(g) $95(\sin x + \tan 2x)^{94} \cdot (\cos x + 2 \sec^2 2x),$

(h) $\dfrac{(1-x)(5x^4+2)+(x^5+2x)}{(1-x)^2},$ (i) $\cos(\cos x) \cdot (-\sin x),$

(j) $\dfrac{1}{1+(1+x)^2},$ (k) $\dfrac{2x}{\sqrt{1-x^4}},$ (l) $92(1+\cos^{-1}x)^{91} \cdot \dfrac{-1}{\sqrt{1-x^2}}.$

PROBLEMS

3. $\dfrac{\pi}{180}\cos x^0,$ $\dfrac{-\pi}{180}\sin x^0,$ $\dfrac{\pi}{180}\sec^2 x^0.$

Section 2.13   EXERCISES

1. (a) $2e^{2x},$ (b) $2xe^{(x^2)},$

(c) $2+\dfrac{1}{2\sqrt{x}}e^{\sqrt{x}},$ (d) $\dfrac{-9}{e^{9x}},$

(e) $-\sin e^{-x}\cdot(-e^{-x}),$ (f) $\dfrac{e^x - e^{-x}}{2}.$

(g) $\dfrac{e^x+e^{-x}}{2}$ (h) $\dfrac{1}{1+x}$ (i) $-1+\ln\dfrac{1}{x}$ (j) 1

(k) $\dfrac{1-\dfrac{1}{x}\cos\dfrac{1}{x}+\sin\dfrac{1}{x}}{x+x\sin\dfrac{1}{x}}$ (l) $2e^{2x}+\sec^2 x$ (m) $10(4e^{-x}+1)(-4e^{-x})$

PROBLEMS

3. (a) A typical term is $\dfrac{\left(1-\frac{1}{n}\right)\left(1-\frac{2}{n}\right)\cdots\left(1-\frac{r-1}{n}\right)}{1\cdot2\cdot3\cdots r}.$

(b) This typical term is less than $(1/2)^{r-1}.$ Continuing the corresponding G. P. to infinity makes its value all the greater and gives the value 3. Hence $[1+(1/n)]^n$ is always less than 3.

5. (a) $x^{(x^x)}[x^{x-1}+x^x\ln x\,(1+\ln x)],$

(b) $-\dfrac{1}{(\log_a x)^2}\cdot\dfrac{1}{x}\cdot\log_a e,$

(c) $\sin x^{\cos x}\left[\dfrac{\cos^2 x}{\sin x}-\sin x\ln\sin x\right],$

(d) $(1+\tan x)^{\sin x}\cdot\left[\dfrac{\sin x\sec^2 x}{1+\tan x}+\cos x\ln(1+\tan x)\right].$

Section 2.16   EXERCISES

1. $-\dfrac{1}{3},-\dfrac{2}{3}.$ 3. (a) Both undefined. (b) 1/2, 0 (c) 0, 2/3.

Chapter 3

Section 3.1   EXERCISES

1. $-\dfrac{1}{\sqrt{2}}, -1, 1$ units per second.   **3.** Infinite.   **5.** Decreasing at 20 sq. in.
per second.   **7.** $\dfrac{\pi}{2}\,(24)^2$ cu. ft. per ft.

PROBLEMS

9. $-\dfrac{30}{\sqrt{300}}$ ft./sec. The rate of fall tends to infinity.   **11.** -2.8 m.p.h.

Section 3.2   EXERCISES

1. $\left(0, \dfrac{9}{2}\right)$.

PROBLEMS

3. (b) $a > 2p$ three normals, $a \leqslant 2p$ one normal (the x-axis).

Section 3.4   EXERCISES

1. (a) max. 4, min. 0,   (b) max. $-\dfrac{5}{2}$, min. 2,   (c) max. 1,
(d) max. $\sqrt{2}$, min. $-\sqrt{2}$,   (e) max. 5, min. -5 (f) min. $-\dfrac{2}{e}$,
(g) max. $\sqrt{2}\,e^{-x}$ for $x = -\dfrac{\pi}{4} + 2\pi n$,   min. $\sqrt{2}\,e^{-x}$ for $x = -\dfrac{\pi}{4} + (2n-1)\pi$,
(h) max. $\sqrt{3}$, min. $-\sqrt{3}$.

PROBLEMS

5. $(2, 2\sqrt{3})$.   **7.** The cylinder with radius $\sqrt{2/3}\,r$.
9. $T = \dfrac{\sqrt{1+x^2}}{12} + \left|\dfrac{4-x}{8}\right|$.   The least time obviously occurs when $x = 4$. Setting
$D_x T = 0$ won't work because of the absolute value function which gives a
sharp corner at the point concerned.   **11.** (a) The angle subtended at the
centre by PQ should be $2/3\,\pi$. (b) The path along the circumference.
13. 144 cu. in.   **15.** Height of cylinder $= 1/3\,h$ yields maximum volume.
17. $\dfrac{200}{3}, \dfrac{200}{3}, \dfrac{100}{3}$ inches.

Section 3.6   EXERCISES

1. For convenience take the line through the origin. Suppose it makes an
angle θ with the x-axis. Let $P(x,y)$ be on the line a distance s from the origin.
Then $x = s \cos \theta$, $y = s \sin \theta$ and the velocity and acceleration are $D_t s$, $D_t^2 s$.

Section 3.7   PROBLEMS

1. (a) $\sqrt{1+\frac{x}{9}}$, (b) $6\left(1+\frac{x}{9}\right)^{3/2}-6$, (c) 4.416 (approx.).

Section 3.8   EXERCISES

3. (a) $\dfrac{6}{(37)^{3/2}}$, (b) 1, (c) 0.

                    PROBLEMS

5. $-\dfrac{D_y{}^2 x}{[1+(D_y x)^2]^{3/2}}$.   The result should be the same as with x, y inter-changed, except for the sign, because the angle is measured in the opposite direction.   **7.** $\dfrac{a}{b^2}$.

Section 3.9   EXERCISES

1. (a) $\dfrac{x^4}{4}$, (b) $12x^{1/3}$, (c) x^2-2x^3, (d) $-2\cos x$, (e) $\sin 2x$,

(f) $-\dfrac{\cos 7x}{7}$, (g) e^{-3x}, (h) $\dfrac{-e^{-4x}}{4}$.

                    PROBLEMS

3. (a) $\dfrac{8}{3}$, (b) 2.

                    EXTRA PROBLEMS

5. 2.96.   **7.** $D_x y \Delta x$ is the increment on the tangent.   **9.** .93.
11. .007 in.   **13.** If $f(a)$, $g(a)$ are not both 0, then $f(x) \neq \Delta f(x)$, $g(x)$ $\neq \Delta g(x)$.   **15.** 64 ounces.

                    Chapter 4

                    EXERCISES

1. (a) $\dfrac{3}{4}2^{4/3}$, (b) $\dfrac{15}{4}$, (c) $32\dfrac{3}{4}$.   **3.** $\dfrac{1}{6}$

                    PROBLEMS

5. $1\dfrac{1}{15}$, $17\dfrac{2}{3}$.

7. 0, because there is just as much area below the x-axis as there is above it.
9. $\dfrac{K}{a}-\dfrac{K}{b}$.   **11.** $\dfrac{f(x)}{g(x)}=\dfrac{f(x)-f(a)}{g(x)-g(a)}=\dfrac{f'(x_1)}{g'(x_1)}$ where $a<x_1<x$, by Problem 10, hence the limit is as required.

Chapter 5

Section 5.1   PROBLEMS

1. $\sin x + 2$ is an anti-derivative of $\cos x$, yet it is not equal to $\displaystyle\int_a^x \cos x \, dx$
for any a.

Section 5.3   EXERCISES

1. $d[f(x) \pm g(x)] = f'(x) dx \pm g'(x) dx$,
   $d(f(x) \cdot g(x)) = f(x) g'(x) dx + f'(x) g(x) dx$,
   $$d \; \frac{f(x)}{g(x)} = \frac{g(x) f'(x) - f(x) g'(x)}{[g(x)]^2} \; dx \, ,$$
   $d \sin x = \cos x \, dx$, $d \cos x = -\sin x \, dx$, $d \tan x = \sec^2 x \, dx$, etc.

3. (a) $\dfrac{x^8}{4}$,   (b) $-2 \cos x$,   (c) $\dfrac{x^2}{4}$,   (d) $\sin x^2$.

Section 5.4   EXERCISES

1. (a) $\dfrac{x}{3} + \dfrac{1}{x}$,   (b) $\dfrac{1}{6}(2x+1)^3$,   (c) $\ln |x+1|$,

   (d) $\sqrt{2t+1}$,   (e) $\dfrac{1}{2} \ln (z^2+2)$,   (f) $\dfrac{1}{60}(3u+4)^{20}$,

   (g) $-\dfrac{1}{4} \ln |2-7y^4|$,   (h) $\dfrac{\sin^3 x}{3}$,   (i) $-\dfrac{1}{3} \ln |\cos 3\theta - 3|$,

   (j) $\ln |1 + \tan t|$,   (k) $-\dfrac{2}{3}(1-e^z)^{3/2}$,   (l) $2\sqrt{1 + \sin t}$,

   (m) $-\ln |\cos x|$,   (n) $\dfrac{1}{2} \sin^{-1} x^2$,   (o) $\dfrac{1}{2} e^{(z^2)}$,

   (p) $\dfrac{(\ln t)^2}{2}$,   (q) $-\cos (x^2 + 4x + 7)$,   (r) $-\cos e^x$,

   (s) $-\dfrac{1}{5} \cos 5x$,   (t) $-\dfrac{1}{2} \cos (z^2+2)$,   (u) $\tan^{-1}x + \dfrac{1}{2} \ln |1+x^2|$.

Section 5.5   PROBLEMS

1. (a) $\dfrac{1}{2} x \sin 2x + \dfrac{1}{4} \cos 2x$,   (b) $x \sin^{-1} x + \sqrt{1-x^2}$,

   (c) $\dfrac{1}{3} x^2 \sin 3x + \dfrac{2}{9} x \cos 3x - \dfrac{2}{27} \sin 3x$,   (d) $-x \cos x + \sin x$,

   (e) $\dfrac{1}{4} x^4 \ln x - \dfrac{1}{16} x^4$,   (f) $x \ln x - x$,

   (g) $x(\ln x)^2 - 2(x \ln x - x)$,   (h) $x^3 e^x - 3x^2 e^x + 6xe^x - 6e^x$,

   (i) $-\dfrac{1}{2} x^2 e^{-x^2} - \dfrac{1}{2} e^{-x^2}$,   (j) $\dfrac{1}{3} x^2 (x^2+1)^{3/2} - \dfrac{2}{15}(x^2+1)^{5/2}$,

   (k) $-\dfrac{1}{2} \dfrac{x^2}{1+x^2} + \dfrac{1}{2} \ln(1+x^2)$,   (l) $\dfrac{e^{-x}}{2}(\sin x - \cos x)$.

Section 5.6 PROBLEMS

1. (a) $2x + 2 \ln |2x - 1|$,

(b) $2 \ln|x - 1| + \ln|x^2 + x + 1|$,

(c) $\frac{1}{16} \ln \left|\frac{x-2}{x+2}\right| + \frac{1}{4x}$,

(d) $\frac{1}{2} \ln |x - 4| - \frac{1}{2} \ln |x - 2|$,

(e) $\frac{1}{2} \tan^{-1} \frac{x+1}{2}$,

(f) $\frac{-13}{x-3} + \frac{3}{2} \ln |x - 1| - \frac{1}{2} \ln |x - 3|$,

(g) $\ln \sqrt{\frac{x-1}{x+1}}$,

(h) $\frac{19}{4} \ln |x - 7| + \frac{1}{4} \ln |x + 1|$,

(i) $\ln |x - 2| - \frac{1}{x-2}$,   (j) $-\frac{1}{4} \ln |1 + x| - \frac{1}{4(1+x)} + \frac{1}{4} \ln |1 - x| + \frac{1}{4(1-x)}$,

(k) $\frac{1}{2} \ln (1 + e^x) - \frac{1}{2} \ln (1 - e^x)$,

(l) $\ln (e^x - 1) - x$,

(m) $2 \ln |x| + \ln (x^2 + 3)$,

(n) $2 \ln |x| - \ln |x^2 + 2| + \frac{\sqrt{2}}{4} \tan^{-1} \frac{x}{\sqrt{2}} + \frac{1}{2} \left[\frac{x}{(2+x^2)}\right]$.

Section 5.9 PROBLEMS

1. (a) $\frac{x}{2} - \frac{1}{4} \sin 2x$,

(b) $\frac{3}{128} x + \frac{\sin 8x}{8.128} - \frac{\sin 4x}{4.32}$,

(c) $\ln \left|\frac{1 + \tan \frac{x}{2}}{1 - \tan \frac{x}{2}}\right|$,

(d) $\frac{3}{8} x + \frac{1}{4} \sin 2x + \frac{1}{32} \sin 4x$,

(e) $-\frac{2}{1 + \tan \frac{x}{2}}$,   (f) $\frac{\cos^3 x}{3} - \cos x$,   (g) $\frac{\sec^5 x}{5} - \frac{\sec^3 x}{3}$,

(h) $\frac{\sin^3 x}{3}$,   (i) $\frac{\tan^3 x}{3} + x - \tan x$,   (j) $\frac{\cos^7 x}{7} - \frac{\cos^5 x}{5}$,

(k) $\frac{\sin (a+bx)}{b} - \frac{\sin^3 (a+bx)}{3b}$,   (l) $\frac{x}{8} - \frac{\sin 4x}{32}$,   (m) $\frac{x}{16} - \frac{\sin^3 2x}{48} - \frac{\sin 4x}{64}$,

(n) $\frac{1}{-3 \sin^3 x} + \frac{1}{\sin x}$,   (o) $\frac{1}{\cos x} + \cos x$.

3. (a) $-\frac{1}{2(m+n)} \cos (m+n) x - \frac{1}{2(m-n)} \cos (m-n) x$,

(b) $-\frac{1}{2(m+n)} \sin (m+n) x = \frac{1}{2(m-n)} \cos (m-n) x$.

Section 5.10 PROBLEMS

1. (a) $\frac{1}{2} \tan^{-1} x + \frac{x}{2(x^2+1)}$,   (b) $-\cos^{-1} (x+1)$,

(c) $\frac{5^4}{\cos^5 t} - \frac{5^5}{3 \cos^3 t}$ where $t = \tan^{-1} \frac{x}{5}$,

(d) $\frac{-5}{16 \sin t}$ where $t = \tan^{-1} \frac{5x}{4}$,

(e) $\dfrac{\sqrt{5}}{50}t+\dfrac{\sqrt{5}}{100}\sin 2t$ where $t=\sec^{-1}\dfrac{x}{5}$,

(f) $3\sin t-3\ln|\sec t+\tan t|$ where $2x=3\cos t$.

Section 5.11   EXERCISES

1. $\int\cos^n x\,dx=\dfrac{\cos^{n-1}x\sin x}{n}+\dfrac{n-1}{n}\int\cos^{n-2}x\,dx;$

$\displaystyle\int\dfrac{1}{\cos^n x}\,dx=\dfrac{\sin x}{(n-1)\cos^{n-1}x}+\dfrac{n-2}{n-1}\int\dfrac{1}{\cos^{n-2}x}\,dx.$

Section 5.12   PROBLEMS

3. (a) $2x^{1/2}+2\ln|x^{1/2}-1|$,

(b) $\dfrac{3}{5}x^{5/6}+\dfrac{3}{8}x^{2/3}+\dfrac{1}{4}x^{1/2}+\dfrac{3}{16}x^{1/3}+\dfrac{3}{16}x^{1/6}+\dfrac{3}{32}\ln|2x^{1/6}-1|$,

(c) $-\dfrac{x}{2}-\dfrac{3}{10}x^{5/6}-\dfrac{3}{16}x^{2/3}-\dfrac{1}{8}x^{1/2}-\dfrac{3}{32}x^{1/3}-\dfrac{3}{32}x^{1/6}-\dfrac{3}{64}\ln|1-2x^{1/6}|$.

Section 5.13   PROBLEMS

1. (a) $x-\ln(1+x)+\dfrac{1}{2}\ln(y^2-9)=C$,

(b) $y-x=C(1+xy)$,

(c) $y=\ln\dfrac{1}{\sin x-C}$,

(d) $(x-3)(y+1)=C$,   (e) $(r^2+1)\sin^2\theta=C$,

(f) $4\ln x+3\ln\dfrac{4}{y+4x}=C$,

(g) $x-2y-4\ln(2x-5y+10)=C$,   (h) $(y-x)e^{y/x}=C$,

(i) $x^2=4y^2\ln\dfrac{y}{C}$,   (j) $\sin\left(\dfrac{y}{x}\right)=Cx$.

3. $v^2=\dfrac{2g\,R^2}{r}+v_0{}^2-2gR$. For $v_0{}^2-2gR\geqslant 0$.

Chapter 6

Section 6.3   EXERCISES

1. $\ln(2+\sqrt{3})$.   3. $2\tanh^{-1}\dfrac{1}{2}-1$.

PROBLEMS

5. $8a$.   7. $\sqrt{2}+\ln(\sqrt{2}+1)$.   9. $8a$.   11. $\sqrt{2}(1-e^{-\pi})$.

Section 6.4 EXERCISES

1. $3\pi a^2$.   3. 36.   5. $\pi \dfrac{a^2}{4}$.

PROBLEMS

7. $\dfrac{3}{8}\pi a^2$.   9. $2a^2$.   11. $a^2\left(\sqrt{3}-\dfrac{\pi}{3}\right)$.   13. $\dfrac{\pi}{4}\,(p^2+q^2)$.

15. $\dfrac{64}{3}\pi a^2$.   17. $2\pi\sqrt{2}+2\pi\sinh^{-1}1$.

19. $\dfrac{8}{3}a^2$.   21. $a^2\,[2\sqrt{3}-\ln(2+\sqrt{3})]$.

Section 6.5 EXERCISES

1. $\dfrac{\pi a^3}{4}$.   3. $\dfrac{4}{3}\pi abc$.   5. 8.

PROBLEMS

7. $\dfrac{1}{3}Ah$.   9. $\dfrac{4}{5}\pi abc$.   11. $\dfrac{\pi^2}{2}$.   13. $\dfrac{1}{6}\alpha a^2$, α being the angle between the planes, a the radius of the base, and h the height of the cone.

15. $\dfrac{2}{3}\,dr^3$.

Section 6.6 EXERCISES

1. $M=6,\ I=18\dfrac{2}{3}$.   3. (a) $\dfrac{r^3}{3}$,   (b) $\dfrac{r^3}{12}$.   5. $\dfrac{\pi}{2}\,r^3$.

PROBLEMS

9. $\dfrac{\pi}{4}\,r^4$.   11. $\dfrac{bh^3}{4}$.   13. $\dfrac{8}{5}\pi r^5$.

Section 6.7 EXERCISES

1. $\left(\dfrac{4a}{3\pi},\dfrac{4b}{3\pi}\right)$.   3. $\left(\dfrac{8}{5},\dfrac{1}{2}\right)$.

PROBLEMS

5. $4\pi^2 ab$.   7. $\dfrac{a^3}{12}b+ab\left(\dfrac{a}{2}+c\right)^2$; a,b being the lengths of the sides and c the distance from the line to the rectangle.

9. (a) $\dfrac{16\pi}{15}$ (b) $\dfrac{6}{15}$.

11. (a) $\bar{x}=\dfrac{2}{3}\dfrac{r}{\alpha}\sin\alpha$, $\bar{y}=\dfrac{2}{3}\dfrac{r}{\alpha}(1-\cos\alpha)$, one side of the sector lying along the $x(\theta=o)$ axis.

(b) $\dfrac{2}{3}\pi r^3(1-\cos\alpha)$. **13.** $\bar{x}=\dfrac{(16)^2 a}{3.35\sqrt{2}\,\pi}$. **15.** $\bar{x}=\dfrac{8}{5}$, $\bar{y}=1$.

Section 6.8   EXERCISES

1. $K\dfrac{h^2}{2}$ ft. lbs.   **3.** 25 in. lbs.

PROBLEMS

5. $K\dfrac{a^2 h^2}{12}$ ft. lbs.   **7.** $\dfrac{K}{S}\dfrac{p^2}{2}$.   **9.** 30 in. lbs.

Section 6.9   EXERCISES

1. 625 (420,000) lbs.

PROBLEMS

3. $4\pi r^2 h w$, where r is the radius of the sphere, h the depth of its centre and w the density of the liquid.

5. $\dfrac{\sqrt{3}}{2}K w a^2$.

7. Distance from centre of pressure to upper edge is $\dfrac{\dfrac{3}{2}hb+b^2}{3\left(h+\dfrac{b}{2}\right)}$ which is not independent of h. It approaches $b/2$ as $h\to\infty$.

Section 6.10   EXERCISES

1. $\dfrac{1}{2}$.   **3.** This requires no calculus. The average can be interpreted as the total moment about the line divided by the total mass.

5. $\dfrac{f(b)-f(a)}{b-a}$ interpreted as slope of chord.   **7.** a.

PROBLEMS

13. $\dfrac{c}{v_2-v_1}\ln\left|\dfrac{v_2}{v_1}\right|$.

Section 6.11   EXERCISES

1. 1.   **3.** e.   **5.** $\dfrac{\pi}{2}$.

PROBLEMS

7. $\left(1,\dfrac{1}{4}\right)$.   **9.** 2.

11. The integral is divergent.

13. For $f(x) = \dfrac{1}{x}$, the left side is 0, while the right side is divergent.

15. Divergent for $K \geqslant 1$, convergent for $K < 1$.

MISCELLANEOUS

17. $K \ln\left|\dfrac{g+w}{w}\right|$.

19. During a time interval t, it travels a distance $v(t)\,\Delta t$. Summing over little intervals between $t=0$ and $t=1$ and taking the limit of the sum gives $\displaystyle\int_0^1 v(t)\,dt$.

Chapter 7

EXERCISES

1. (a) $-x - \dfrac{x^2}{2} - \dfrac{x^3}{3} - \cdots - \dfrac{x^n}{n} - \cdots$,

  (b) $x + \dfrac{1}{2}\dfrac{x^3}{3} + \dfrac{1\cdot 3}{2\cdot 4}\dfrac{x^5}{5} + \dfrac{1\cdot 3\cdot 5}{2\cdot 4\cdot 6}\dfrac{x^7}{7} + \cdots$.

Section 7.1   EXERCISES

1. (a) $2n$, (b) $(-1)^{n-1}(2n-1)$, (c) $\dfrac{n}{2n-1}$, (d) $(-1)^{n-1}\dfrac{x^{n-1}}{n!}$,

  (e) $\dfrac{1}{n^2}$, (f) $(-1)^{n-1}\dfrac{x^{n-1}}{(3n-2)!}$.

Section 7.7   EXERCISES

1. (a) convergent, (b) divergent, (c) convergent, (d) convergent,

  (e) convergent, (f) divergent,

  (g) $(-1)^{n-1}\dfrac{1}{\sqrt{2n-1}}$, convergent,

  (h) $\dfrac{1}{\sqrt{2n-1}}$, divergent,

  (i) $\dfrac{n!}{3^n}$, divergent,

  (j) $\dfrac{(-1)^{n-1}(n+2)}{n(n+1)}$, convergent,

  (k) $\dfrac{n+2}{n(n+1)}$, divergent.

Section 7.10   EXERCISES

1. (a) $-1 < x < 1$, (b) $-1 \leqslant x < 1$,

  (c) $-\dfrac{1}{2} < x < \dfrac{1}{2}$, (d) $-1 < x \leqslant 1$, (e) $-1 \leqslant x < 1$.

Section 7.15   EXERCISES

1. 0.3103.   **3.** $p \leqslant 1$.

PROBLEMS

5. (a) convergent, (b) divergent, (c) divergent.

7. $1 + \dfrac{1}{2^2} + \dfrac{1}{3^2} + \cdots + \dfrac{1}{n^2} + \cdots$.

9. $x + \dfrac{x^3}{3!} + \dfrac{x^5}{5!} + \dfrac{x^7}{7!} + \cdots + \dfrac{x^{2n-1}}{(2n-1)!} + \cdots$.

11. $(x-1) - \dfrac{(x-1)^2}{2} + \dfrac{(x-1)^3}{3} - \cdots + (-1)^{2n-1} \dfrac{(x-1)^n}{n} + \cdots, \; 0 < x \leqslant 2$.

13. $\ln 2 + \dfrac{1}{2}(x-2) - \dfrac{1}{2^2}\dfrac{(x-2)^2}{2!} + \dfrac{2}{2^3}\dfrac{(x-2)^3}{3!} - \dfrac{6}{2^4}\dfrac{(x-2)^4}{4!} + \cdots$

$+ (-1)^n \dfrac{1}{2^{n-1}} \dfrac{(x-2)^{n-1}}{(n-1)}, \; 0 < x \leqslant 4$.

Chapter 8

Section 8.2   EXERCISES

1. (a) $2xz + y$, (b) $x + z^2$, (c) $x^2 + 2yz$.   **3.** (a) 2, (b) -2.

Section 8.3   EXERCISES

1. (a) 4, (b) 8.

Section 8.5   EXERCISES

1. $\cos xy \, (2yt + x)$.   **3.** $(2y - 3x)\cos t - (2x - 3y)\sin t$.

PROBLEMS

5. 7.6.

7. (a) $(y^2 + 2xy)\,\Delta x + (2xy + x^2)\,\Delta y$,

(b) $2e^y z \Delta x + 2xe^y z \Delta y + 2xe^y \Delta z$,

(c) $(\sin v - v \sin u)\,\Delta u + (u \cos v + \cos u)\,\Delta v$,

(d) $6(x^2 + y^4)^5 \, 2x \, \Delta x + 6\,(x^2 + y^4)^5 \, 4y^3 \, \Delta y$,

(e) $(z + 3x^2 y^2)\,\Delta x + (2yz + 2x^3 y)\,\Delta y + (x + y^2)\,\Delta z$,

(f) $e^{x/y} \dfrac{1}{y} \Delta x - e^{x/y} \dfrac{x}{y^2} \Delta y$.

Section 8.6   EXERCISES

1. $-\dfrac{3x^2 + 3y^2}{6xy + 4y}$.

3. $-\dfrac{x}{9z}, \; -\dfrac{4y}{9z}$.

5. $-\dfrac{2ax+2by+2d}{2bx+2cy+2e}$.

7. $-\dfrac{Bz+Cy}{Ay+Bx}, -\dfrac{Az+Cx}{Ay+Bx}$.

Section 8.7   PROBLEMS

3. (a) minimum at $(4,-2)$,   (b) minimum at $(-3,3)$,
(c) minimum at (a,a) if $a>0$, maximum at (a,a) if $a<0$,
(d) minimum at $(1,1)$.

5. $x=y=\sqrt[3]{2K}$, $z=\dfrac{\sqrt[3]{K}}{2^{2/3}}$.

Section 8.8   EXERCISES

1. 5/2 second quadrant, $-5/2$ fourth quadrant.

3. $\dfrac{1}{25}\left(\dfrac{3\sqrt{3}}{2}+2\right)$.

5. $\tan^{-1}\dfrac{x}{y}$, $a\sqrt{x^2+y^2}$.

7. $\dfrac{e}{2\sqrt{2}}(\sqrt{3}-1)$.

Section 8.9   EXERCISES

1. $6x+2y+3z=49$.   **3.** $4x+2y-z=56$.   **5.** $5x+4y+3z=22$.

Chapter 9

Section 9.8   EXERCISES

1. 3.   **3.** 42.   **5.** $\dfrac{1}{2}(e-1)^2$.   **7.** $\dfrac{4}{3}a^3$.   **9.** $a^2\,[2\sqrt{3}-\ln(2+\sqrt{3})]$.

11. $\dfrac{27}{5}$.   **13.** $\dfrac{768}{35}$.   **15.** $\dfrac{a^2}{3}$.

PROBLEMS

17. $\dfrac{8}{3}\pi a^3$.   **19.** $\dfrac{3}{35}$.   **21.** $\dfrac{55}{28}2^{2/5}\pi$.   **23.** $\dfrac{1}{2}$.   **25.** $\dfrac{1}{2}\pi a^4$.

27. $\dfrac{1}{6}abc$.

A Table of Integrals

Integrals Containing $ax + b$

1. $\int \dfrac{x\,dx}{ax + b} = \dfrac{1}{a^2}\left[ax + b - b\,\ln|ax + b|\right].$

2. $\int \dfrac{x\,dx}{(ax + b)^2} = \dfrac{1}{a^2}\left[\dfrac{b}{ax + b} + \ln|ax + b|\right].$

3. $\int \dfrac{x\,dx}{(ax + b)^3} = \dfrac{1}{a^2}\left[\dfrac{-1}{ax + b} + \dfrac{b}{2(ax + b)^2}\right].$

Integrals Containing $ax^2 + bx + c$

4. $\int \dfrac{dx}{ax^2 + bx + c} = \dfrac{2}{\sqrt{4ac - b^2}}\,\text{Arc tan}\,\dfrac{2ax + b}{\sqrt{4ac - b^2}}, \qquad b^2 - 4ac < 0$

$\qquad = \dfrac{1}{\sqrt{b^2 - 4ac}}\,\ln\left|\dfrac{2ax + b - \sqrt{b^2 - 4ac}}{2ax + b + \sqrt{b^2 - 4ac}}\right| \qquad b^2 - 4ac > 0.$

5. $\int \dfrac{dx}{(ax^2 + bx + c)^2} = \dfrac{2ax + b}{(4ac - b^2)(ax^2 + bx + c)} + \dfrac{2a}{4ac - b^2}\int \dfrac{dx}{ax^2 + bx + c}.$

Integrals Containing $\sqrt{ax + b}$

6. $\int x\sqrt{ax + b}\,dx = \dfrac{2}{a^2}\left[\dfrac{(ax + b)^{5/2}}{5} - \dfrac{b(ax + b)^{3/2}}{3}\right].$

7. $\int x^2\sqrt{ax + b}\,dx = \dfrac{2}{a^3}\left[\dfrac{(ax + b)^{7/2}}{7} - \dfrac{2b(ax + b)^{5/2}}{5} + \dfrac{b^2(ax + b)^{3/2}}{3}\right].$

8. $\int \dfrac{dx}{x\sqrt{ax + b}} = \dfrac{1}{\sqrt{b}}\,\ln\left|\dfrac{\sqrt{ax + b} - \sqrt{b}}{\sqrt{ax + b} + \sqrt{b}}\right|, \qquad b > 0.$

$\qquad = \dfrac{2}{\sqrt{-b}}\,\text{Tan}^{-1}\dfrac{\sqrt{ax + b}}{\sqrt{-b}}, \qquad b < 0.$

9. $\int \dfrac{dx}{x^2\sqrt{ax + b}} = -\dfrac{\sqrt{ax + b}}{bx} - \dfrac{a}{2b}\int \dfrac{dx}{x\sqrt{ax + b}}.$

Integrals Containing $\sqrt{x^2 \pm a^2}$

10. $\displaystyle\int \frac{dx}{(x^2 \pm a^2)^{3/2}} = \pm\frac{1}{a^2}\frac{x}{\sqrt{x^2 \pm a^2}}.$

11. $\displaystyle\int \frac{dx}{(x^2 \pm a^2)^{5/2}} = \frac{1}{a^4}\left[\frac{x}{\sqrt{x^2 \pm a^2}} - \frac{1}{3}\frac{x^3}{(x^2 \pm a^2)^{3/2}}\right].$

12. $\displaystyle\int \frac{x^2\,dx}{\sqrt{x^2 \pm a^2}} = \frac{x\sqrt{x^2 \pm a^2}}{2} \mp \frac{a^2}{2}\ln|x + \sqrt{x^2 \pm a^2}|.$

13. $\displaystyle\int \frac{x^2\,dx}{(x^2 \pm a^2)^{3/2}} = -\frac{x}{\sqrt{x^2 \pm a^2}} + \ln|x + \sqrt{x^2 \pm a^2}|.$

14. $\displaystyle\int \frac{x^2\,dx}{(x^2 \pm a^2)^{5/2}} = \pm\frac{1}{3a^2}\frac{x^3}{(x^2 \pm a^2)^{3/2}}.$

15. $\displaystyle\int \frac{dx}{x\sqrt{x^2 + a^2}} = -\frac{1}{a}\ln\frac{a + \sqrt{x^2 + a^2}}{|x|}.$

16. $\displaystyle\int \frac{dx}{x\sqrt{x^2 - a^2}} = \frac{1}{a}\,\mathrm{Sec}^{-1}\frac{x}{a}, \qquad a > 0.$

17. $\displaystyle\int \frac{dx}{x^2\sqrt{x^2 \pm a^2}} = \mp\frac{\sqrt{x^2 \pm a^2}}{a^2 x}.$

18. $\displaystyle\int (x^2 \pm a^2)^{3/2}\,dx = \frac{x}{4}(x^2 \pm a^2)^{3/2} \pm \frac{3}{8}a^2 x\sqrt{x^2 \pm a^2} + \frac{3}{8}a^4\ln|x + \sqrt{x^2 \pm a^2}|.$

19. $\displaystyle\int \frac{\sqrt{x^2 + a^2}}{x}\,dx = \sqrt{x^2 + a^2} - a\ln\frac{a + \sqrt{x^2 + a^2}}{|x|}.$

20. $\displaystyle\int \frac{\sqrt{x^2 - a^2}}{x}\,dx = \sqrt{x^2 - a^2} - a\,\mathrm{Sec}^{-1}\frac{x}{a}, \qquad a > 0.$

21. $\displaystyle\int \frac{\sqrt{x^2 \pm a^2}}{x^2}\,dx = -\frac{\sqrt{x^2 \pm a^2}}{x} + \ln|x + \sqrt{x^2 \pm a^2}|.$

22. $\displaystyle\int x^2\sqrt{x^2 \pm a^2}\,dx = \frac{x}{4}(x^2 \pm a^2)^{3/2} \mp \frac{a^2 x\sqrt{x^2 \pm a^2}}{8} - \frac{a^4}{8}\ln|x + \sqrt{x^2 \pm a^2}|.$

Integrals Containing $\sqrt{a^2 - x^2}$

23. $\displaystyle\int \frac{dx}{(a^2 - x^2)^{3/2}} = \frac{1}{a^2}\frac{x}{\sqrt{a^2 - x^2}}.$

24. $\displaystyle\int \frac{x^2\,dx}{\sqrt{a^2 - x^2}} = -\frac{x\sqrt{a^2 - x^2}}{2} + \frac{a^2}{2}\,\mathrm{Sin}^{-1}\frac{x}{a}, \qquad a > 0.$

25. $\displaystyle\int \frac{x^2\,dx}{(a^2 - x^2)^{3/2}} = \frac{x}{\sqrt{a^2 - x^2}} - \mathrm{Sin}^{-1}\frac{x}{a}, \qquad a > 0.$

26. $\int \dfrac{dx}{x\sqrt{a^2 - x^2}} = -\dfrac{1}{a} \ln \left| \dfrac{a + \sqrt{a^2 - x^2}}{x} \right|.$

27. $\int \dfrac{dx}{x(a^2 - x^2)^{3/2}} = \dfrac{1}{a^2\sqrt{a^2 - x^2}} - \dfrac{1}{a^3} \ln \left| \dfrac{a + \sqrt{a^2 - x^2}}{x} \right|.$

28. $\int \dfrac{dx}{x^2\sqrt{a^2 - x^2}} = -\dfrac{\sqrt{a^2 - x^2}}{a^2 x}.$

29. $\int \dfrac{dx}{x^2(a^2 - x^2)^{3/2}} = \dfrac{1}{a^4} \left[-\dfrac{\sqrt{a^2 - x^2}}{x} + \dfrac{x}{\sqrt{a^2 - x^2}} \right].$

30. $\int (a^2 - x^2)^{3/2} \, dx = \dfrac{x}{4} (a^2 - x^2)^{3/2} + \dfrac{3}{8} a^2 x \sqrt{a^2 - x^2} + \dfrac{3}{8} a^4 \operatorname{Sin}^{-1} \dfrac{x}{a}, \qquad a > 0.$

31. $\int \dfrac{\sqrt{a^2 - x^2}}{x} \, dx = \sqrt{a^2 - x^2} - a \ln \left| \dfrac{a + \sqrt{a^2 - x^2}}{x} \right|.$

32. $\int \dfrac{\sqrt{a^2 - x^2}}{x^2} \, dx = -\dfrac{\sqrt{a^2 - x^2}}{x} - \operatorname{Sin}^{-1} \dfrac{x}{a}, \qquad a > 0.$

33. $\int \dfrac{(a^2 - x^2)^{3/2}}{x} \, dx = \dfrac{(a^2 - x^2)^{3/2}}{3} + a^2\sqrt{a^2 - x^2} - a^3 \ln \left| \dfrac{a + \sqrt{a^2 - x^2}}{x} \right|.$

34. $\int x^2\sqrt{a^2 - x^2} \, dx = -\dfrac{x(a^2 - x^2)^{3/2}}{4} + \dfrac{a^2 x \sqrt{a^2 - x^2}}{8} + \dfrac{a^4}{8} \operatorname{Sin}^{-1} \dfrac{x}{a}, \qquad a > 0.$

Trigonometric Integrals

35. $\int \sin^3 x \, dx = \dfrac{\cos^3}{3} - \cos x.$

36. $\int \sin^4 x \, dx = \dfrac{3x}{8} - \dfrac{\sin 2x}{4} + \dfrac{\sin 4x}{32}.$

37. $\int \cos^3 x \, dx = \sin x - \dfrac{\sin^3 x}{3}.$

38. $\int \cos^4 x \, dx = \dfrac{3x}{8} + \dfrac{\sin 2x}{4} + \dfrac{\sin 4x}{32}.$

39. $\int \tan^3 x \, dx = \dfrac{\tan^2 x}{2} + \ln | \cos x |.$

40. $\int \tan^4 x \, dx = \dfrac{1}{3} \tan^3 x - \tan x + x.$

41. $\int \sec^3 x \, dx = \dfrac{1}{2} \sec x \tan x + \dfrac{1}{2} \ln | \sec x + \tan x |.$

42. $\int \sec^4 x \, dx = \tan x + \dfrac{1}{3} \tan^3 x.$

Miscellaneous Integrals

43. $\displaystyle\int x^n \ln x \, dx = x^{n+1} \left[\frac{\ln x}{n+1} - \frac{1}{(n+1)^2} \right].$

44. $\displaystyle\int \frac{\ln x}{x^n} \, dx = -\frac{\ln x}{(n-1)x^{n-1}} - \frac{1}{(n-1)^2 x^{n-1}}.$

45. $\displaystyle\int x e^{ax} \, dx = e^{ax} \left[\frac{x}{a} - \frac{1}{a^2} \right].$

46. $\displaystyle\int x^2 e^{ax} \, dx = e^{ax} \left[\frac{x^2}{a} - \frac{2x}{a^2} + \frac{2}{a^3} \right].$

47. $\displaystyle\int x \sin x \, dx = \sin x - x \cos x.$

48. $\displaystyle\int x^2 \sin x \, dx = 2x \sin x - (x^2 - 2) \cos x.$

49. $\displaystyle\int x \sin^2 x \, dx = \frac{x^2}{4} - \frac{x \sin 2x}{4} - \frac{\cos 2x}{8}.$

50. $\displaystyle\int x^2 \sin^2 x \, dx = \frac{x^3}{6} - \left(\frac{x^2}{4} - \frac{1}{8} \right) \sin 2x - \frac{x \cos 2x}{4}.$

51. $\displaystyle\int x \cos^2 x \, dx = \frac{x^2}{4} + \frac{x \sin 2x}{4} + \frac{\cos 2x}{8}.$

52. $\displaystyle\int x^2 \cos^2 x \, dx = \frac{x^3}{6} + \left(\frac{x^2}{4} - \frac{1}{8} \right) \sin 2x + \frac{x \cos 2x}{4}.$

53. $\displaystyle\int e^{ax} \sin bx \, dx = \frac{e^{ax}(a \sin bx - b \cos bx)}{a^2 + b^2}.$

54. $\displaystyle\int e^{ax} \cos bx \, dx = \frac{e^{ax}(a \cos bx + b \sin bx)}{a^2 + b^2}.$

55. $\displaystyle\int \sin^n x \, dx = -\frac{\sin^{n-1} x \cos x}{n} + \frac{n-1}{n} \int \sin^{n-2} x \, dx.$

56. $\displaystyle\int \cos^n x \, dx = \frac{\cos^{n-1} x \sin x}{n} + \frac{n-1}{n} \int \cos^{n-2} x \, dx.$

57. $\displaystyle\int \tan^n x \, dx = \frac{\tan^{n-1} x}{n-1} - \int \tan^{n-2} x \, dx.$

58. $\displaystyle\int \cot^n x \, dx = -\frac{\cot^{n-1} x}{n-1} - \int \cot^{n-2} x \, dx.$

59. $\displaystyle\int \sec^n x \, dx = \frac{\sec^{n-2} x \tan x}{n-1} + \frac{n-2}{n-1} \int \sec^{n-2} x \, dx.$

60. $\displaystyle\int x^n e^{ax} \, dx = \frac{x^n e^{ax}}{a} - \frac{n}{a} \int x^{n-1} e^{ax} \, dx.$

Index

Symbols

Subjects